THE CUNY
MATH EXAM REVIEW

REVISED EDITION

RICHARD N. AUFMANN
Palomar College, California

The math drills and
practice tests you need
to point you in the
right direction.

HOUGHTON MIFFLIN COMPANY BOSTON NEW YORK

Custom Publishing Editor: Todd Corbin
Custom Publishing Production Manager: Tina Kozik
Project Coordinator: Anisha Palmer
Cover Design: Althea Chen
Cover Art: PhotoDisc, Althea Chen

This book contains select works from existing Houghton Mifflin Company resources and was produced by Houghton Mifflin Custom Publishing for collegiate use. As such, those adopting and/or contributing to this work are responsible for editorial content, accuracy, continuity and completeness.

Printed in the United States of America.

ISBN-13: 978-0-618-69088-6
ISBN-10: 0-618-69088-3
N-05625

5 6 7 8 9 – BMP – 08 07

Houghton Mifflin
Custom Publishing

222 Berkeley Street • Boston, MA 02116
Address all correspondence and order information to the above address.

All of us at Houghton Mifflin would like to thank the many CUNY math professors for their input and direction in putting this math drill and preparation book together. Without their help, this exam review book would not have been possible.

Table of Contents

Name: _____ Date: _____

1. What is 16,012 divided by 46?
   A) 348, remainder 4.
   B) 358, remainder 4.
   C) 348, remainder 3.
   D) 358, remainder 5.
   E) 348, remainder 7.

2. Subtract: $11,192 - 5,452$.
   A) 5,740
   B) 5,850
   C) 6,840
   D) 16,644
   E) 5,751

3. Write the following number in standard form: nine million two hundred seventy-eight thousand six hundred forty-seven.
   A) 2,786,479
   B) 9,278,647
   C) 7,864,792
   D) 8,647,927
   E) None of the above.

4. The tennis coach at a high school purchased a video camera that costs $1,138 and made a down payment of $313. Find the amount that remains to be paid.
   A) $814
   B) $925
   C) $825
   D) $826
   E) $925

5. What is 847 added to 1,969?
   A) 2,826
   B) 1,122
   C) 3,816
   D) 2,816
   E) 2,715

Sample Test
Prepared by Houghton Mifflin

6. Round the number 24,331,300 to the millions place.
    A) 2,433,130
    B) 24,300,000
    C) 24,331,000
    D) 24,330,000
    E) 24,000,000

7. Find the product of 7,945 and 154,992.
    A) 1,231,411,440
    B) 1,221,411,440
    C) 1,221,211,440
    D) 1,230,301,440
    E) 1,231,181,440

8. Find the product of 7, 13, and 19.
    A) 1,729
    B) 1,719
    C) 1,749
    D) 1,629
    E) 1,839

9. Graph the number 1 on the number line.
   A)

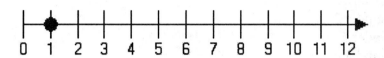

   B)

   C)

   D)

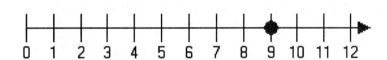

   E)

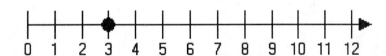

Sample Test
Prepared by Houghton Mifflin

10. Divide: $9\overline{)1,326}$.
   A) 147, remainder 5.
   B) 97, remainder 3.
   C) 147, remainder 3.
   D) 97, remainder 5.
   E) 147, remainder 4.

11. Multiply:

       2,362
   ×   234

   A) 549,708
   B) 532,708
   C) 530,708
   D) 552,708
   E) 555,708

12. What is 1,554 divided by 2?
   A) 767
   B) 766
   C) 777
   D) 797
   E) 808

13. Multiply:

       9,869
   ×   5

   A) 49,345
   B) 48,345
   C) 47,345
   D) 46,245
   E) 45,245

Sample Test
Prepared by Houghton Mifflin

14. Name the place value of the digit 8 in this number: 22,856,041.
    A) Thousands
    B) Ten-thousands
    C) Hundred-thousands
    D) Millions
    E) Ten-millions

15. What is 4,558 increased by 4,327?
    A) 7,785
    B) 231
    C) 9,885
    D) 8,985
    E) 8,885

16. Divide: $6\overline{)216,024}$.
    A) 46,204
    B) 35,004
    C) 26,004
    D) 47,004
    E) 36,004

17. Find the sum of 75, 231, 2, and 14,323.
    A) 14,531
    B) 14,631
    C) 14,732
    D) 14,632
    E) 14,621

18. What is 25,405 more than 7,733?
    A) 17,672
    B) 33,138
    C) 34,138
    D) 33,148
    E) 32,128

Sample Test
Prepared by Houghton Mifflin

19. Subtract:

$$
\begin{array}{r}
3,157 \\
-\ 2,563 \\
\hline
\end{array}
$$

  A) 594
  B) 604
  C) 583
  D) 5,720
  E) 694

20. What is the word name for: 1,646,287?
  A) six million two hundred forty-six thousand one hundred eighty-seven
  B) one million six hundred eighty-seven thousand two hundred forty-six
  C) one million six hundred forty-six thousand two hundred eighty-seven
  D) six million two hundred eighty-seven thousand one hundred forty-six
  E) None of the above.

21. Add:

$$
\begin{array}{r}
84,351 \\
93,216 \\
+\ \ 33,961 \\
\hline
\end{array}
$$

  A) 211,528
  B) 210,428
  C) 221,628
  D) 212,627
  E) 210,517

22. What is 1,761 divided by 7? Round to the nearest ten.
  A) 260
  B) 240
  C) 250
  D) 270
  E) 280

Sample Test
Prepared by Houghton Mifflin

23. Rob Hill owns a compact car that averages 48 miles on 1 gallon of gas. How many miles could the car travel on 16 gallons of gas?
    A) 758
    B) 768
    C) 868
    D) 968
    E) 568

24. Find 5,481 decreased by 2,752.
    A) 2,829
    B) 2,629
    C) 2,619
    D) 8,233
    E) 2,729

25. Divide: $356\overline{)12,477}$.
    A) 35, remainder 17.
    B) 32, remainder 17.
    C) 35, remainder 16.
    D) 32, remainder 19.
    E) 33, remainder 21.

26. What is 8,424 times 2?
    A) 16,848
    B) 15,838
    C) 16,748
    D) 16,948
    E) 15,848

27. Write the following number in expanded form: 3,930,958.
    A) 30,000,000 + 900,000 + 30,000 + 900 + 50 + 8
    B) 3 + 90 + 300 + 90,000 + 500,000 + 8,000,000
    C) 30,000,000 + 9,000,000 + 300,000 + 9,000 + 500 + 80
    D) 3,000,000 + 900,000 + 30,000 + 900 + 50 + 8
    E) None of the above.

Sample Test
Prepared by Houghton Mifflin

28. A farmer harvested 30,000 pounds of avocados from one grove and 15,000 pounds of avocados from another grove. The avocados were packed in shipping boxes with 30 pounds in each box. How many boxes were needed to pack the avocados?
    A) 1,500
    B) 1,000
    C) 3,000
    D) 3,500
    E) 2,500

29. Add: $170 + 91 + 14,201 + 886$.
    A) 15,338
    B) 14,348
    C) 15,448
    D) 15,358
    E) 15,348

30. You have $537 in your checking account. If you write a check for $262, how much is left in your checking account?
    A) $264
    B) $285
    C) $275
    D) $276
    E) $375

31. Place the correct symbol, $<$, $>$, or $=$, between the two numbers: 5205 ? 5025.
    A) $5205 < 5025$
    B) $5205 > 5025$
    C) $5205 = 5025$

32. The perimeter of a triangle is the sum of the lengths of the three sides of the triangle. Find the perimeter of a triangle that has sides that measure 35 inches, 30 inches, and 28 inches.
    A) 93
    B) 92
    C) 84
    D) 82
    E) 94

Sample Test
Prepared by Houghton Mifflin

33. The table below shows the annual expenditures, in a recent year, of the average household in the United States.

Average Annual Household Expenses

Housing	$11,713
Food	$4810
Insurance	$3381
Health care	$1903
Entertainment	$1746
Other	$5366

Source: Bureau of Labor Statistics
Consumer Expenditure Survey

What is the average monthly expense for food? Round your answer to the nearest dollar.
A) $398
B) $406
C) $409
D) $401
E) $394

34. Find the total of 479, 15, and 5,294.
A) 5,789
B) 5,678
C) 5,888
D) 5,788
E) 5,687

35. What is 67,506 less than 94,041?
A) 36,535
B) 27,535
C) 26,535
D) 161,547
E) 26,645

Sample Test
Prepared by Houghton Mifflin

36. Subtract:

        36,421
     − 24,585

    A) 61,006
    B) 11,936
    C) 11,736
    D) 11,836
    E) 12,836

37. The area of a rectangle is equal to the product of the length of the rectangle times its width. Find the area of a rectangle that has a length of 38 meters and a width of 17 meters.
    A) 646 square meters
    B) 636 square meters
    C) 626 square meters
    D) 746 square meters
    E) 766 square meters

38. Find the product of 2, 6 and 2.
    A) 24
    B) 14
    C) 44
    D) 29
    E) 9

39. Subtract:

        6,496
     − 4,075

    A) 2,521
    B) 2,311
    C) 2,432
    D) 3,421
    E) 2,421

Sample Test
Prepared by Houghton Mifflin

40. Suppose that in a recent year, there were 96,190 twin births in a country, 6,008 triplet births, 642 quadruplet deliveries, and 77 quintuplet and higher-order multiple births. Find the total number of multiple births during the year.
    A) 102,917 multiple births
    B) 101,917 multiple births
    C) 103,927 multiple births
    D) 92,917 multiple births
    E) 102,817 multiple births

Sample Test
Prepared by Houghton Mifflin

Answer Key

1. A
2. A
3. B
4. C
5. D
6. E
7. A
8. A
9. A
10. C
11. D
12. C
13. A
14. C
15. E
16. E
17. B
18. B
19. A
20. C
21. A
22. C
23. B
24. E
25. A
26. A
27. D
28. A
29. E
30. C
31. B
32. A
33. D
34. D
35. C
36. D
37. A
38. A
39. E
40. A

Sample Test
Prepared by Houghton Mifflin

Name: _____ Date: _____

1. Add:

$$\frac{4}{7} + \frac{13}{7}$$

A) $2\frac{3}{7}$

B) $\frac{17}{7}$

C) $\frac{3}{14}$

D) $2\frac{3}{14}$

E)   Both A and B.

2. Add:

$$4\frac{1}{2}$$
$$+ \quad 4\frac{7}{10}$$
$$\overline{}$$

A) $9\frac{1}{5}$

B) $10\frac{1}{5}$

C) $10\frac{2}{9}$

D) $9\frac{2}{9}$

E) $10\frac{2}{11}$

Sample Test
Prepared by Houghton Mifflin

3. Write the improper fraction $\dfrac{27}{3}$ as a mixed number or a whole number.

   A) 9

   B) $9\dfrac{2}{3}$

   C) $8\dfrac{1}{3}$

   D) $11\dfrac{2}{3}$

   E) 11

4. Identify the following fraction as a proper fraction, an improper fraction, or a mixed number.

   $9\dfrac{6}{11}$

   A) Improper fraction

   B) Mixed number

   C) Proper fraction

5. Add:

   $\dfrac{7}{22}+\dfrac{1}{10}$

   A) $1\dfrac{23}{55}$

   B) $\dfrac{23}{55}$

   C) $\dfrac{23}{110}$

   D) $2\dfrac{23}{110}$

   E) None of the above.

Sample Test
Prepared by Houghton Mifflin

6. Add:

$$\frac{5}{9} + \frac{13}{18}$$

A) $1\frac{5}{27}$

B) $\frac{14}{9}$

C) $\frac{5}{18}$

D) $1\frac{5}{18}$

E) $2\frac{5}{18}$

7. Identify the following fraction as a proper fraction, an improper fraction, or a mixed number.

$$\frac{31}{19}$$

A) Improper fraction
B) Mixed number
C) Proper fraction

8. Add:

$$5\frac{6}{7}$$
$$+ \quad 8$$
$$\overline{}$$

A) $14\frac{18}{19}$

B) $14\frac{6}{7}$

C) $13\frac{6}{7}$

D) $13\frac{18}{19}$

E) $14\frac{18}{23}$

Sample Test
Prepared by Houghton Mifflin

9. Write an equivalent fraction with the given denominator.

$$\frac{4}{13} = \frac{?}{52}$$

A) $\frac{23}{52}$

B) $\frac{17}{52}$

C) $\frac{20}{52}$

D) $\frac{4}{52}$

E) $\frac{16}{52}$

10. Find $4\frac{4}{7}$ more than $1\frac{1}{4}$.

A) $6\frac{23}{30}$

B) $6\frac{23}{28}$

C) $6\frac{23}{26}$

D) $5\frac{23}{26}$

E) $5\frac{23}{28}$

Sample Test
Prepared by Houghton Mifflin

11. Add:

$$11\frac{2}{3}+2$$

A) $14\frac{2}{3}$

B) $13\frac{2}{3}$

C) $14\frac{54}{79}$

D) $13\frac{54}{79}$

E) $14\frac{54}{83}$

Sample Test
Prepared by Houghton Mifflin

12. Shade $2\dfrac{3}{4}$ out of 3 circles.

A)

B)

C)

D)

E)

13. Add:

$$7\frac{6}{11}+4\frac{1}{4}$$

A) $12\frac{5}{6}$

B) $12\frac{35}{44}$

C) $11\frac{35}{44}$

D) $11\frac{5}{6}$

E) $12\frac{35}{46}$

14. Find the sum of $\frac{5}{6}$, $\frac{1}{6}$, and $\frac{7}{8}$.

A) $3\frac{7}{16}$

B) $3\frac{7}{8}$

C) $1\frac{7}{16}$

D) $1\frac{7}{8}$

E) None of the above.

Sample Test
Prepared by Houghton Mifflin

15. Express the shaded portion of the circle as a fraction.

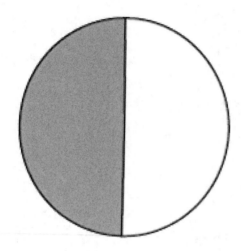

A) $\dfrac{2}{5}$

B) $\dfrac{7}{10}$

C) $\dfrac{2}{3}$

D) $\dfrac{3}{4}$

E) $\dfrac{1}{2}$

16. Find the sum of $\dfrac{7}{16}$, $\dfrac{3}{16}$, and $\dfrac{11}{16}$.

A) $1\dfrac{5}{16}$

B) $\dfrac{5}{8}$

C) $\dfrac{5}{32}$

D) $1\dfrac{5}{32}$

E) Both A and B.

Sample Test
Prepared by Houghton Mifflin

17. Add:

$6 + 2\dfrac{2}{5}$

A) $9\dfrac{2}{5}$

B) $8\dfrac{2}{5}$

C) $9\dfrac{5}{12}$

D) $8\dfrac{5}{12}$

E) $9\dfrac{5}{13}$

18. Write the mixed number $6\dfrac{2}{3}$ as an improper fraction.

A) $\dfrac{8}{3}$

B) $\dfrac{10}{3}$

C) $\dfrac{20}{3}$

D) 6

E) $\dfrac{2}{3}$

19. Find the total of $\dfrac{5}{8}$, $\dfrac{3}{8}$, and $\dfrac{7}{9}$.

A) $1\dfrac{7}{18}$

B) $3\dfrac{7}{9}$

C) $1\dfrac{7}{9}$

D) $3\dfrac{7}{18}$

E) None of the above.

Sample Test
Prepared by Houghton Mifflin

20. Find the sum of $2\frac{1}{2}$ and $3\frac{5}{6}$.

   A) $6\frac{1}{3}$

   B) $7\frac{1}{3}$

   C) $7\frac{6}{17}$

   D) $6\frac{6}{17}$

   E) $7\frac{6}{19}$

21. Add: $3\frac{2}{3} + 3\frac{4}{7} + 1\frac{5}{7}$.

   A) $9\frac{20}{21}$

   B) $8\frac{20}{21}$

   C) $8\frac{10}{21}$

   D) $9\frac{10}{21}$

   E)   None of the above.

22. Add:

$$\frac{1}{11} + \frac{5}{11}$$

   A) $\frac{6}{22}$

   B) $\frac{6}{11}$

   C) $\frac{4}{11}$

   D) $\frac{4}{22}$

   E)   1

Sample Test
Prepared by Houghton Mifflin

23. Add:

$$5$$

$$+ \quad 2\frac{3}{8}$$

A) $8\frac{9}{26}$

B) $8\frac{3}{8}$

C) $8\frac{9}{22}$

D) $7\frac{9}{22}$

E) $7\frac{3}{8}$

24. Express the shaded portion of the circle as an improper fraction.

 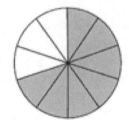

A) $\frac{8}{3}$

B) $\frac{17}{10}$

C) $\frac{11}{4}$

D) $\frac{3}{2}$

E) $\frac{5}{2}$

Sample Test
Prepared by Houghton Mifflin

25. Write an equivalent fraction with the given denominator.

$$3 = \frac{?}{3}$$

A) $\frac{9}{3}$

B) $\frac{10}{3}$

C) $\frac{12}{3}$

D) $\frac{3}{3}$

E) $\frac{16}{3}$

26. Find the sum of $\frac{11}{25}$, $\frac{9}{25}$, and $\frac{11}{25}$.

A) $1\frac{3}{25}$

B) $\frac{31}{25}$

C) $\frac{3}{25}$

D) $1\frac{6}{25}$

E) Both B and D.

27. Add:

$$\frac{7}{12} + \frac{5}{12}$$

A) 12

B) $\frac{1}{2}$

C) $\frac{1}{6}$

D) $\frac{1}{12}$

E) 1

Sample Test
Prepared by Houghton Mifflin

28. Add:

$$\frac{5}{7} + \frac{4}{7} + \frac{3}{7}$$

A) $1\frac{5}{7}$

B) $\frac{9}{7}$

C) $\frac{5}{14}$

D) $1\frac{5}{14}$

E) Both A and B.

29. Add:

$$\frac{6}{13} + \frac{17}{26} + \frac{37}{52}$$

A) $2\frac{43}{52}$

B) $3\frac{43}{52}$

C) $1\frac{43}{52}$

D) $\frac{43}{52}$

E) None of the above.

30. Express the shaded portion of the circle as a mixed number.

 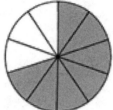

A) $1\dfrac{7}{10}$

B) $2\dfrac{2}{3}$

C) $2\dfrac{3}{4}$

D) $1\dfrac{1}{2}$

E) $1\dfrac{2}{5}$

31. What is $4\dfrac{4}{7}$ added to $9\dfrac{3}{8}$?

A) $13\dfrac{53}{56}$

B) $14\dfrac{53}{56}$

C) $14\dfrac{53}{54}$

D) $13\dfrac{53}{54}$

E) $14\dfrac{53}{58}$

32. Identify the following fraction as a proper fraction, an improper fraction, or a mixed number.

$\dfrac{1}{6}$

A) Improper fraction
B) Mixed number
C) Proper fraction

Sample Test
Prepared by Houghton Mifflin

33. Find the total of 2, $5\frac{7}{8}$, and $5\frac{5}{8}$.

A) $15\frac{1}{2}$

B) $13\frac{1}{2}$

C) $13\frac{1}{4}$

D) $15\frac{1}{4}$

E) None of the above.

34. What is $\frac{1}{2}$ added to $\frac{7}{12}$?

A) $2\frac{1}{12}$

B) $1\frac{1}{12}$

C) $1\frac{1}{24}$

D) $3\frac{4}{7}$

E) $\frac{4}{7}$

35. Write the fraction in simplest form.

$\frac{5}{24}$

A) $\frac{5}{24}$

B) $\frac{5}{48}$

C) $\frac{5}{12}$

D) 1

E) 0

Sample Test
Prepared by Houghton Mifflin

36. The course of a yachting race is in the shape of a triangle with sides that measure $3\frac{1}{6}$ miles, $5\frac{7}{12}$ miles, and $5\frac{3}{8}$ miles. Find the total length of the course.

A) $16\frac{1}{16}$

B) $16\frac{1}{8}$

C) $14\frac{1}{16}$

D) $14\frac{1}{8}$

E) $13\frac{1}{16}$

37. You are working on a part-time job for $20 per hour. You worked 4, $2\frac{1}{2}$, $2\frac{1}{2}$, $3\frac{1}{2}$, and $6\frac{1}{2}$ hours during the last five days.

a. Find the total number of hours you worked during the last five days.
b. Find your total wages for the five days.

A) (a) 18 hours; (b) $381 pay.
B) (a) 18 hours; (b) $380 pay.
C) (a) 19 hours; (b) $379 pay.
D) (a) 18 hours; (b) $379 pay.
E) (a) 19 hours; (b) $380 pay.

38. Fred Thomson worked $3\frac{1}{3}$ hours of overtime on Monday, $3\frac{3}{5}$ hours on Wednesday, $2\frac{2}{3}$ hours on Friday, and $7\frac{2}{5}$ hours on Saturday.

a. Find the total number of overtime hours worked during the week.
b. At an overtime wage of $20 per hour, how much overtime pay does Fred receive?

A) (a) 16 overtime hours; (b) $339 overtime pay.
B) (a) 16 overtime hours; (b) $340 overtime pay.
C) (a) 17 overtime hours; (b) $339 overtime pay.
D) (a) 17 overtime hours; (b) $340 overtime pay.
E) None of the above.

Sample Test
Prepared by Houghton Mifflin

39. Three cylindrical shaped parts are joined at their ends to form a mechanical shaft. If the individual parts are $\frac{1}{4}$ inches, $\frac{3}{8}$ inches, and $\frac{7}{16}$ inches long, respectively, what is the total length of the shaft?

A) $3\frac{1}{32}$ inches

B) $3\frac{1}{16}$ inches

C) $1\frac{1}{32}$ inches

D) $1\frac{1}{16}$ inches

E) None of the above.

40. A table 29 inches high has a top that is $1\frac{3}{8}$ inches thick. Find the total thickness of the tabletop after a $2\frac{1}{16}$-inch veneer is applied.

A) $3\frac{7}{16}$

B) $4\frac{7}{16}$

C) $4\frac{4}{9}$

D) $3\frac{4}{9}$

E) $4\frac{28}{65}$

Answer Key

1. E
2. A
3. A
4. B
5. B
6. D
7. A
8. C
9. E
10. E
11. B
12. A
13. C
14. D
15. E
16. A
17. B
18. C
19. C
20. A
21. B
22. B
23. E
24. B
25. A
26. E
27. E
28. A
29. C
30. A
31. A
32. C
33. B
34. B
35. A
36. D
37. E
38. D
39. D
40. A

Sample Test
Prepared by Houghton Mifflin

Name: _____ Date: _____

1. A nurse earns a salary of $1006 for a 40-hour week. This week the nurse worked 17 hours of overtime at a rate of $37.73 for each hour of overtime worked.
   a. Find the nurse's overtime pay.
   b. Find the nurse's total income for the week.
   A) (a) $641.41; (b) $1647.41
   B) (a) $678.03; (b) $2040.53
   C) (a) $661.44; (b) $1784.19
   D) (a) $641.41; (b) $2040.53
   E) (a) $678.03; (b) $1647.41

2. Two mechanical shafts are joined together, end-to-end. Their combined length is 11.54 inches. If one of the shafts is 7.07 inches long, how long is the other shaft?
   A) 5.47 in.
   B) 5.57 in.
   C) 3.37 in.
   D) 4.57 in.
   E) None of the above.

3. Subtract:

   $$\begin{array}{r} 0.05 \\ -\ 0.0138 \\ \hline \end{array}$$

   A) 0.1363
   B) 0.0363
   C) 0.0261
   D) 0.0362
   E) 0.2462

4. The perimeter of a triangle is the sum of the lengths of the three sides of the triangle. Find the perimeter of a triangle that has sides that measure 3.9 meters, 5.9 meters, and 8.1 meters.
   A) 17.8 meters
   B) 19 meters
   C) 17.9 meters
   D) 18.9 meters
   E) 18.1 meters

Sample Test
Prepared by Houghton Mifflin

5. Add:

    4.399 + 28.21 + 7.377
    A) 29.785
    B) 39.986
    C) 38.885
    D) 40.098
    E) 40.096

6. Divide 226.884 by 7.3.
    A) 31.08
    B) 30.98
    C) 30.99
    D) 31.18
    E) 32.19

7. You have $1547.41 in your checking account. You make deposits of $228.29, $44.59, $1163.55, and $30.03. Find the amount in your checking account after you have made the deposits if no money has been withdrawn.
    A) $3123.87
    B) $3023.89
    C) $3114.99
    D) $3014.99
    E) $3013.87

8. Anne is building bookcases that are 2.9 feet long. How many complete shelves can be cut from a 9-foot board?
    A) 4
    B) 2
    C) 3
    D) 5
    E) None of the above.

9. A shaft is built from three cylindrical parts joined end-to-end. Find the length of the shaft if the individual parts are 1.91 inches, 2.13 inches, and 2.43 inches long, respectively.
    A) 6.47 in.
    B) 5.46 in.
    C) 6.36 in.
    D) 7.58 in.
    E) 7.57 in.

Sample Test
Prepared by Houghton Mifflin

10. Divide:

    $4.5\overline{)37.8}$

    A) 8.5
    B) 8.4
    C) 7.4
    D) 9.4
    E) 9.5

11. Add:

    $$\begin{array}{r} 6.952 \\ + \ 5.4 \\ \hline \end{array}$$

    A) 12.352
    B) 11.252
    C) 12.242
    D) 12.553
    E) 12.453

12. Divide. Round your answer to the nearest whole number.

    $7.458 \div 0.178$

    A) 31
    B) 32
    C) 42
    D) 62
    E) 21.0

13. The manager of the Edgewater Cafe takes a reading of the cash register tape each hour. At 2:00 P.M. the tape read $1187.55. At 3:00 P.M. the tape read $1669.92. Find the amount of sales between 2:00 P.M. and 3:00 P.M.

    A) $483.38
    B) $482.37
    C) $602.37
    D) $692.47
    E) None of the above.

Sample Test
Prepared by Houghton Mifflin

14. Multiply: 5.55 x 10,000.
    A) 55,500
    B) 5550
    C) 555
    D) 55.5
    E) 555,000

15. What is the word name for: 0.066?
    A) sixty-six hundredths
    B) thirty-six hundredths
    C) sixty-six thousandths
    D) thirty-six thousandths
    E) None of the above.

16. Write this fraction as a decimal: $\dfrac{25}{1000}$
    A) 25
    B) 0.25
    C) 2.5
    D) 0.025
    E) None of the above

17. Add:

    43.838 + 2.87 + 2.763
    A) 49.471
    B) 49.369
    C) 49.358
    D) 59.572
    E) 54.582

Sample Test
Prepared by Houghton Mifflin

18. Write this decimal as a fraction: 0.317
    A) $\dfrac{317}{10}$

    B) $\dfrac{317}{100}$

    C) $\dfrac{317}{1000}$

    D) $\dfrac{317}{10,000}$

    E) None of the above.

19. Bay Area Rental Cars charges $14 a day and $0.15 per mile for renting a car. You rented a car for 4 days and drove 256 miles. Find the total cost of renting the car.
    A) $105.50
    B) $104.40
    C) $95.50
    D) $93.40
    E) $94.40

20. Ramon, a high school football player, gained 168 yards on 30 carries in a high school football game. Find the average number of yards gained per carry. Round to the nearest hundredth.
    A) 6.70 yards
    B) 5.59 yards
    C) 5.49 yards
    D) 6.60 yards
    E) 5.60 yards

21. Add:

$$
\begin{array}{r}
87.1 \\
4.008 \\
+\ 977.22 \\
\hline
\end{array}
$$

    A) 1068.328
    B) 1058.228
    C) 1067.218
    D) 1068.118
    E) 1068.348

Sample Test
Prepared by Houghton Mifflin

22. Name the place value of the digit 6 in this number: 58.905396
    A) Ten-thousandths
    B) Hundred-thousandths
    C) Millionths
    D) Thousandths
    E) Hundredths

23. Subtract:

$$
\begin{array}{r}
9.339 \\
-\ 6.217 \\
\hline
\end{array}
$$

    A) 3.122
    B) 3.123
    C) 3.012
    D) 3.224
    E) 3.332

24. The perimeter of a square is equal to four times the length of a side of the square. Find the perimeter of a square whose side measures 1.7 meters.
    A) 3.4 m
    B) 17.8 m
    C) 6.8 m
    D) 4.4 m
    E) None of the above.

25. Add:

    0.757 + 6.21 + 71.412
    A) 78.378
    B) 78.379
    C) 78.377
    D) 78.38
    E) 78.48

Sample Test
Prepared by Houghton Mifflin

26. Multiply:

> 64.767
> x 7.9
> ----------

- A) 521.8693
- B) 511.5583
- C) 511.6593
- D) 512.7694
- E) 521.7794

27. Multiply: 1.56×10^4.
- A) 15.6
- B) 1560
- C) 156
- D) 15,600
- E) 156,000

28. Divide:

$53,028 \div 10^3$

- A) 53028
- B) 5.3028
- C) 530.28
- D) 5302.8
- E) 53.028

29. What is 0.10946 divided by 0.26?
- A) 0.421
- B) 0.411
- C) 0.432
- D) 0.522
- E) 1.531

30. Find the product of 9, 0.74, and 6.7.
- A) 45.833
- B) 44.622
- C) 46.723
- D) 46.632
- E) 45.822

Sample Test
Prepared by Houghton Mifflin

31. Subtract:
    896.45 − 17.414
    A) 879.146
    B) 879.036
    C) 878.036
    D) 980.146
    E) 979.136

32. Earl is 56 years old and is buying $90,000 of life insurance for an annual premium of $693.11. If he pays each annual premium in 12 equal instalments, how much is each monthly payment? Round your answer to the nearest cent.
    A) $58.76
    B) $57.75
    C) $57.65
    D) $57.76
    E) $58.86

33. Find the product of 6.27 and 0.651.
    A) 4.08177
    B) 4.071569
    C) 4.07976
    D) 4.08289
    E) 4.09388

34. Subtract:

       198.85
    −   14.741

    A) 184.109
    B) 184.12
    C) 174.008
    D) 284.119
    E) 194.319

35. Round 81.416 to the nearest hundredth.
    A) 81.43
    B) 81.42
    C) 81.41
    D) 0.42
    E) 0.44

Sample Test
Prepared by Houghton Mifflin

36. A case of diet cola costs $6.75. If there are 24 cans in a case, find the cost per can. Round to the nearest cent.
    A) $0.38
    B) $0.18
    C) $0.28
    D) $1.48
    E) $1.28

37. An electric motor costing $335.21 has an operating cost of $0.021 for 1 hour of operation. Find the cost to run the motor for 40 hours.
    A) $0.84
    B) $1.94
    C) $2.85
    D) $281.58
    E) $291.68

38. Subtract:
    $59.434 - 8.4329$
    A) 52.1011
    B) 50.8911
    C) 61.0111
    D) 51.0011
    E) 61.0011

39. You bought a car for $3500 down and made payments of $395.77 for 48 months.
    a. Find the amount of the payments over the 48 months.
    b. Find the total cost of the car.
    A) (a) $18,996.96; (b) $22,871.60
    B) (a) $17,954.51; (b) $22,871.60
    C) (a) $19,735.31; (b) $22,979.08
    D) (a) $18,996.96; (b) $22,496.96
    E) (a) $17,954.51; (b) $22,496.96

40. Grace Herrera owned 399.739 shares of a mutual fund on January 1. On December 31 of the same year, she had 487.661 shares. What was the increase in the number of shares Grace owned during that year?
    A) 66.922
    B) 197.922
    C) 76.922
    D) 87.922
    E) None of the above.

Sample Test
Prepared by Houghton Mifflin

Answer Key

1. A
2. E
3. D
4. C
5. B
6. A
7. E
8. C
9. A
10. B
11. A
12. C
13. B
14. A
15. C
16. D
17. A
18. C
19. E
20. E
21. A
22. C
23. A
24. C
25. B
26. C
27. D
28. E
29. A
30. B
31. B
32. D
33. A
34. A
35. B
36. C
37. A
38. E
39. D
40. D

Sample Test
Prepared by Houghton Mifflin

Name: _____ Date: _____

1. Evaluate $(-3)^5(-8)^2(-4)^3$.
   A) –124,416
   B) –995,328
   C) 995,328
   D) –1,990,656
   E) 124,416

2. Evaluate $(-5)^4$.
   A) 625
   B) –625
   C) –1024
   D) 1024
   E) 20

3. Simplify:
   $$(-4)^{1/2}$$
   A) –2
   B) 2
   C) $-\dfrac{1}{2}$
   D) $\dfrac{1}{2}$
   E) Not a real number

4. Simplify:
   $$\left(\dfrac{49}{25}\right)^{-3/2}$$
   A) $\dfrac{125}{343}$
   B) $\dfrac{343}{125}$
   C) $-\dfrac{125}{343}$
   D) $-\dfrac{343}{125}$
   E) Not a real number

5. Write the mass of Mercury, which is approximately 330,000,000,000,000,000,000,000 kg, in scientific notation.
  A) 3.3×10^{25}
  B) 3.3×10^{24}
  C) 3.3×10^{22}
  D) 3.3×10^{23}
  E) 3.3×10^{21}

6. Evaluate $(-5)^3$.
  A) -125
  B) 125
  C) -243
  D) 243
  E) 15

7. Evaluate -5^4.
  A) 625
  B) -625
  C) 1024
  D) -1024
  E) 20

8. Write the number 0.00005 in scientific notation.
  A) 5×10^{-3}
  B) 5×10^{-4}
  C) 5×10^{-5}
  D) 5×10^{-6}
  E) 5×10^{-7}

9. Simplify:
   $36^{3/2}$
  A) 6
  B) 216
  C) 36
  D) $\dfrac{1}{6}$
  E) $\dfrac{1}{36}$

Sample Test
Prepared by Houghton Mifflin

10. Simplify:

$$(-16)^{1/2}$$

    A) -4

    B) 4

    C) $-\dfrac{1}{4}$

    D) $\dfrac{1}{4}$

    E) Not a real number

11. Write the number 0.0058 in scientific notation.

    A) 5.8×10^{-1}

    B) 5.8×10^{-2}

    C) 5.8×10^{-3}

    D) 5.8×10^{-4}

    E) 5.8×10^{-5}

12. Evaluate $3(-3)^4$

    A) 243

    B) -243

    C) -192

    D) 192

    E) 36

13. Evaluate 4^5.

    A) 625

    B) 1024

    C) 4

    D) 5

    E) 20

14. Write the number 0.005 in scientific notation.

    A) 5×10^{-1}

    B) 5×10^{-2}

    C) 5×10^{-3}

    D) 5×10^{-4}

    E) 5×10^{-5}

Sample Test
Prepared by Houghton Mifflin

15. Simplify:

$36^{3/2}$

A) 6

B) 216

C) 36

D) $\dfrac{1}{6}$

E) $\dfrac{1}{36}$

16. Simplify:

$(-9)^{3/2}$

A) −27

B) 27

C) $-\dfrac{1}{27}$

D) $\dfrac{1}{27}$

E) Not a real number

17. Write the number 580,000,000,000 in scientific notation.

A) 5.8×10^9

B) 5.8×10^{10}

C) 5.8×10^{11}

D) 5.8×10^{12}

E) 5.8×10^{13}

18. Simplify:

$8^{1/3}$

A) 2

B) 8

C) 4

D) $\dfrac{1}{2}$

E) $\dfrac{1}{8}$

19. Simplify:

$216^{-2/3}$

A) 6

B) 216

C) −36

D) $\dfrac{1}{6}$

E) $\dfrac{1}{36}$

20. Simplify:

$64^{1/3}$

A) 4

B) 64

C) 16

D) $\dfrac{1}{4}$

E) $\dfrac{1}{64}$

21. Write the number 59,000,000,000 in scientific notation.

A) 5.9×10^{8}

B) 5.9×10^{9}

C) 5.9×10^{10}

D) 5.9×10^{11}

E) 5.9×10^{12}

22. Simplify:

$8^{-2/3}$

A) 2

B) 8

C) −4

D) $\dfrac{1}{2}$

E) $\dfrac{1}{4}$

23. Evaluate $(-3)^4(-4)^2$.
    A) 324
    B) 1296
    C) −1296
    D) 2592
    E) −324

24. Simplify:

    $4^{3/2}$
    A) 2
    B) 8
    C) 4
    D) $\dfrac{1}{2}$
    E) $\dfrac{1}{4}$

25. Write the number 0.00046 in scientific notation.
    A) 4.6×10^{-2}
    B) 4.6×10^{-3}
    C) 4.6×10^{-4}
    D) 4.6×10^{-5}
    E) 4.6×10^{-6}

26. Evaluate 3^5.
    A) 125
    B) 243
    C) 3
    D) 5
    E) 15

Sample Test
Prepared by Houghton Mifflin

27. Simplify:

$$\left(\frac{25}{16}\right)^{-3/2}$$

   A) $\dfrac{64}{125}$

   B) $\dfrac{125}{64}$

   C) $-\dfrac{64}{125}$

   D) $-\dfrac{125}{64}$

   E)   Not a real number

28. Evaluate $(-5)^4(-8)^2(-5)^3$.
   A)   625,000
   B)   5,000,000
   C)   −5,000,000
   D)   10,000,000
   E)   −625,000

29. Write the number 490,000,000,000 in scientific notation.
   A) 4.9×10^9
   B) 4.9×10^{10}
   C) 4.9×10^{11}
   D) 4.9×10^{12}
   E) 4.9×10^{13}

30. Write the mass of Venus, which is approximately 4,870,000,000,000,000,000,000,000 kg, in scientific notation.
   A) 4.87×10^{26}
   B) 4.87×10^{25}
   C) 4.87×10^{23}
   D) 4.87×10^{24}
   E) 4.87×10^{22}

Sample Test
Prepared by Houghton Mifflin

31. Evaluate -4^5.
   A) 1024
   B) −1024
   C) 625
   D) −625
   E) 20

32. Simplify:
   $216^{-2/3}$
   A) 6
   B) 216
   C) −36
   D) $\dfrac{1}{6}$
   E) $\dfrac{1}{36}$

33. Simplify:
   $\left(\dfrac{36}{16}\right)^{-3/2}$
   A) $\dfrac{8}{27}$
   B) $\dfrac{27}{8}$
   C) $-\dfrac{8}{27}$
   D) $-\dfrac{27}{8}$
   E) Not a real number

34. The electric charge on an electron is 0.00000000000000000016 coulomb. Write this number in scientific notation.
   A) 1.6×10^{-19} coulomb
   B) 1.6×10^{-18} coulomb
   C) 1.6×10^{-20} coulomb
   D) 1.6×10^{-14} coulomb
   E) 1.6×10^{-22} coulomb

Sample Test
Prepared by Houghton Mifflin

35. Write the number 5,500,000,000,000 in scientific notation.
    A) 5.5×10^{10}
    B) 5.5×10^{11}
    C) 5.5×10^{12}
    D) 5.5×10^{13}
    E) 5.5×10^{14}

36. Evaluate $(-2)^3(-4)^2$.
    A) -32
    B) -128
    C) 128
    D) -256
    E) 32

37. Evaluate $3(-5)^3$
    A) -375
    B) 375
    C) -729
    D) 729
    E) 45

38. Write the number 0.0059 in scientific notation.
    A) 5.9×10^{-1}
    B) 5.9×10^{-2}
    C) 5.9×10^{-3}
    D) 5.9×10^{-4}
    E) 5.9×10^{-5}

39. Evaluate $(-4)^3(-5)^2(-4)^3$.
    A) $-20,480$
    B) $-102,400$
    C) $102,400$
    D) $-204,800$
    E) $20,480$

40. Write the number 460,000,000,000,000 in scientific notation.

    A) 4.6×10^{12}

    B) 4.6×10^{13}

    C) 4.6×10^{14}

    D) 4.6×10^{15}

    E) 4.6×10^{16}

Sample Test
Prepared by Houghton Mifflin

Answer Key

1. C
2. A
3. E
4. A
5. D
6. A
7. B
8. C
9. B
10. E
11. C
12. A
13. B
14. C
15. B
16. E
17. C
18. A
19. E
20. A
21. C
22. E
23. B
24. B
25. C
26. B
27. A
28. C
29. C
30. D
31. B
32. E
33. A
34. A
35. C
36. B
37. A
38. C
39. C
40. C

Sample Test
Prepared by Houghton Mifflin

Sample Test
Prepared by Houghton Mifflin

Name: _____ Date: _____

1. Solve. Round to the nearest hundredth, if necessary.

   $$\frac{3}{10} = \frac{n}{9}$$

   A) 2.70
   B) 2.75
   C) 3.75
   D) 3.72
   E) None of the above.

2. Write the phrase as a rate in simplest form.
   402 feet on 24 seconds

   A) $\dfrac{67\ \text{feet}}{4\ \text{seconds}}$

   B) $\dfrac{67\ \text{seconds}}{4\ \text{feet}}$

   C) $\dfrac{268\ \text{feet}}{16\ \text{seconds}}$

   D) $\dfrac{268\ \text{seconds}}{16\ \text{feet}}$

   E) $\dfrac{134\ \text{seconds}}{8\ \text{feet}}$

3. Determine whether the proportion is true or false.

   $$\frac{42\ \text{miles}}{30\ \text{hours}} = \frac{15\ \text{miles}}{9\ \text{hours}}$$

   A) True
   B) False

4. Solve.

   $$\frac{16}{n} = \frac{8}{14}$$

   A) 42
   B) 3.5
   C) 14
   D) 28
   E) None of the above.

Sample Test
Prepared by Houghton Mifflin

5. Solve.

$$\frac{55}{45} = \frac{n}{54}$$

A) 66

B) 5.5

C) 33

D) 55

E) None of the above.

6. Write the comparison as a ratio in simplest form using a fraction, a colon (:), and the word *to*.

21 gallons to 9 gallons

A) $\frac{28}{12}$ 28 : 12   28 to 12

B) $\frac{3}{7}$ 3 : 7   3 to 7

C) $\frac{14}{6}$ 14 : 6   14 to 6

D) $\frac{6}{14}$ 6 : 14   6 to 14

E) $\frac{7}{3}$ 7 : 3   7 to 3

7. Solve. Round to the nearest hundredth, if necessary.

$$\frac{1}{2} = \frac{12}{n}$$

A) 23.87

B) 24.20

C) 24.00

D) 25.87

E) None of the above.

8. Determine whether the proportion is true or false.

$$\frac{9}{7} = \frac{18}{14}$$

A) True

B) False

Sample Test
Prepared by Houghton Mifflin

9. Determine whether the proportion is true or false.

$$\frac{1 \text{ feet}}{2 \text{ cups}} = \frac{6 \text{ feet}}{12 \text{ cups}}$$

A) True
B) False

10. A pre-election survey showed that 2 out of every 3 eligible voters would cast ballots in the county election. At this rate, how many people in a county of 300,000 eligible voters would vote in the election?
A) 210,000
B) 190,000
C) 220,000
D) 200,000
E) None of the above.

11. Assume that Regency Computer produced 5000 zip disks for $23,140.8. Of the disks made, 179 did not meet company standards.
   a. How many disks did meet company standards?
   b. What was the cost per disk for those disks that met company standards?
   A) a) 4821; b) $\dfrac{\$4.80}{\text{disk}}$
   B) a) 179; b) $\dfrac{4.80 \text{ disks}}{\$1}$
   C) a) 179; b) $\dfrac{\$4.83}{\text{disk}}$
   D) a) 4821; b) $\dfrac{4.83 \text{ disks}}{\$1}$
   E) a) 4821; b) $\dfrac{\$4.78}{\text{disk}}$

12. Determine whether the proportion is true or false.

$$\frac{21}{24} = \frac{16}{18}$$

A) True
B) False

Sample Test
Prepared by Houghton Mifflin

13. Determine whether the proportion is true or false.

$$\frac{6 \text{ feet}}{60 \text{ seconds}} = \frac{5 \text{ feet}}{50 \text{ seconds}}$$

A) True
B) False

14. A 60-year-old male can obtain $10,000 of life insurance for $35.53 per month. At this rate, what is the monthly cost of $20,000 of life insurance?
A) $71.06
B) $60.81
C) $76.06
D) $63.81
E) None of the above.

15. Solve.

$$\frac{36}{42} = \frac{30}{n}$$

A) 3.5
B) 35
C) 21
D) 42
E) None of the above.

16. Carlos Capasso owns 70 shares of Texas Utilities that pay dividends of $130. At this rate, what dividend would Carlos receive after buying 560 additional shares of Texas Utilities?
A) $1070
B) $1320
C) $970
D) $1120
E) None of the above.

17. A car travels 68.5 miles on 3 gallons of gas. Find the distance that the car can travel on 10 gallons of gas. Round to the nearest hundredth.
A) 238.83 miles
B) 222.83 miles
C) 228.33 miles
D) 234.33 miles
E) None of the above.

Sample Test
Prepared by Houghton Mifflin

18. Rita Sterling bought a computer system for $3600. Five years later she sold the computer for $800. Find the ratio of the amount she received for the computer to the cost of the computer.

A) $\dfrac{2}{9}$

B) $\dfrac{9}{2}$

C) $\dfrac{4}{9}$

D) $\dfrac{9}{4}$

E) $\dfrac{2}{18}$

19. The average price of a 30-second commercial during a popular sitcom last year was $407,400. Find the price per second.

A) $\dfrac{13580 \text{ seconds}}{\$1}$

B) $\dfrac{\$13580}{\text{second}}$

C) $\dfrac{\$407,400}{30 \text{ seconds}}$

D) $\dfrac{407,400 \text{ seconds}}{\$30}$

E) $\dfrac{\$814,800}{60 \text{ seconds}}$

20. The price of gasoline jumped from \$2.24 to \$2.88 in 1 year.
    a. What is the increase in the price of gasoline?
    b. What is the ratio of the increase in price to the original price?

    A) a) \$0.64; b) $\dfrac{7}{2}$

    B) a) \$5.12; b) $\dfrac{2}{7}$

    C) a) \$0.64; b) $\dfrac{2}{7}$

    D) a) \$5.12; b) $\dfrac{7}{2}$

    E) a) \$0.64; b) $\dfrac{1}{7}$

21. A bank requires a monthly payment of \$31.85 on a \$2900 loan. At the same rate, find the monthly payment on an \$8700 loan. Round to the nearest hundredth.
    A) 95.55
    B) 90.05
    C) 90.55
    D) 105.55
    E) None of the above.

22. Determine whether the proportion is true or false.
    $$\dfrac{3 \text{ feet}}{10 \text{ rolls}} = \dfrac{10 \text{ feet}}{29 \text{ rolls}}$$
    A) True
    B) False

Sample Test
Prepared by Houghton Mifflin

23. Write the comparison as a ratio in simplest form using a fraction, a colon (:), and the word *to*.

    66 dollars to 54 dollars

    A) $\dfrac{11}{9}$ 11 : 9   11 to 9

    B) $\dfrac{9}{11}$ 9 : 11   9 to 11

    C) $\dfrac{44}{36}$ 44 : 36   44 to 36

    D) $\dfrac{36}{44}$ 36 : 44   36 to 44

    E) $\dfrac{33}{27}$ 33 : 27   33 to 27

24. An automobile was driven 379.32 miles on 10.9 gallons of gas. Find the number of miles driven per gallon of gas.

    A) $\dfrac{34.8 \text{ gallons}}{\text{mile}}$

    B) $\dfrac{34.8 \text{ miles}}{\text{gallon}}$

    C) $\dfrac{379.32 \text{ miles}}{10.9 \text{ gallons}}$

    D) $\dfrac{379.32 \text{ gallons}}{10.9 \text{ miles}}$

    E) $\dfrac{382.8 \text{ gallons}}{11 \text{ miles}}$

25. Write the phrase as a rate in simplest form.
    $378 for 24 packs

    A) $\dfrac{\$252}{16 \text{ packs}}$

    B) $\dfrac{\$4}{63 \text{ packs}}$

    C) $\dfrac{\$63}{4 \text{ packs}}$

    D) $\dfrac{\$16}{252 \text{ packs}}$

    E) $\dfrac{\$315}{20 \text{ packs}}$

26. Write the phrase as a rate in simplest form.
    385 gallons in 19 hours

    A) $\dfrac{1155 \text{ hours}}{57 \text{ gallons}}$

    B) $\dfrac{385 \text{ hours}}{19 \text{ gallons}}$

    C) $\dfrac{1155 \text{ gallons}}{57 \text{ hours}}$

    D) $\dfrac{385 \text{ gallons}}{19 \text{ hours}}$

    E) $\dfrac{2310 \text{ hours}}{114 \text{ gallons}}$

27. Write the phrase as a unit rate.
    $292.60 for 209 ounces

    A) $\dfrac{310.80 \text{ ounces}}{\$222}$

    B) $\dfrac{1.4 \text{ ounces}}{\$1}$

    C) $\dfrac{\$292.60}{209 \text{ ounces}}$

    D) $\dfrac{292.60 \text{ ounces}}{\$209}$

    E) $\dfrac{\$1.4}{\text{ounce}}$

Sample Test
Prepared by Houghton Mifflin

28. Determine whether the proportion is true or false.

$$\frac{9 \text{ hours}}{\$6} = \frac{15 \text{ hours}}{\$10}$$

    A) True
    B) False

29. A house with an original value of $50,000 increase in value to $70,000 in 5 years.
    a. Find the increase in the value of the house.
    b. What is the ratio of the increase in value to the original value of the house?

    A)   a) $120,000; b) $\dfrac{2}{5}$

    B)   a) $20,000; b) $\dfrac{2}{5}$

    C)   a) $20,000; b) $\dfrac{5}{2}$

    D)   a) $120,000; b) $\dfrac{5}{2}$

    E)   a) $20,000; b) $\dfrac{1}{5}$

30. Solve. Round to the nearest hundredth, if necessary.

$$\frac{n}{18} = \frac{3}{2}$$

    A) 27.05
    B) 37.05
    C) 25.95
    D) 27.00
    E) None of the above.

31. Solve.

$$\frac{n}{12} = \frac{12}{16}$$

    A) 6
    B) 12
    C) 9
    D) 1.5
    E) None of the above.

Sample Test
Prepared by Houghton Mifflin

32. Solve. Round to the nearest hundredth, if necessary.

$$\frac{2.3}{2.7} = \frac{n}{21}$$

   A) 27.94
   B) 17.89
   C) 16.84
   D) 17.94
   E) None of the above.

33. Write the phrase as a unit rate.
    84 feet in 6 seconds

   A) $\dfrac{14 \text{ feet}}{\text{second}}$

   B) $\dfrac{14 \text{ seconds}}{\text{foot}}$

   C) $\dfrac{84 \text{ feet}}{6 \text{ seconds}}$

   D) $\dfrac{84 \text{ seconds}}{6 \text{ feet}}$

   E) $\dfrac{112 \text{ seconds}}{8 \text{ feet}}$

34. Write the phrase as a rate in simplest form.
    121 miles on 14 gallons

   A) $\dfrac{121 \text{ miles}}{14 \text{ gallons}}$

   B) $\dfrac{121 \text{ gallons}}{14 \text{ miles}}$

   C) $\dfrac{726 \text{ miles}}{84 \text{ gallons}}$

   D) $\dfrac{726 \text{ gallons}}{84 \text{ miles}}$

   E) $\dfrac{484 \text{ gallons}}{56 \text{ miles}}$

Sample Test
Prepared by Houghton Mifflin

35. You own 180 shares of stock in a computer company. The company declares a stock split of 5 shares for every 3 owned. How many shares of stock will you own after the stock split?
    A) 311
    B) 300
    C) 305
    D) 310
    E) None of the above.

36. Solve. Round to the nearest hundredth, if necessary.
    $$\frac{33}{n} = \frac{2}{3}$$
    A) 49.60
    B) 49.70
    C) 49.37
    D) 51.37
    E) None of the above.

37. You drove 196.65 miles in 4.5 hours. Find the number of miles you drove per hour.
    A) $\dfrac{43.7 \text{ miles}}{\text{hour}}$

    B) $\dfrac{43.7 \text{ hours}}{\text{mile}}$

    C) $\dfrac{196.65 \text{ miles}}{4.5 \text{ hours}}$

    D) $\dfrac{196.65 \text{ hours}}{4.5 \text{ miles}}$

    E) $\dfrac{485.07 \text{ hours}}{11.1 \text{ miles}}$

38. Ron Stokes uses 1 pounds of fertilizer for every 100 square feet of lawn for landscape maintenance. At this rate, how many pounds of fertilizer did he use on a lawn that measures 4500 square feet? Round to the nearest hundredth.
    A) 55
    B) 56
    C) 50
    D) 45
    E) None of the above.

Sample Test
Prepared by Houghton Mifflin

39. Write the phrase as a unit rate.
     $146.40 earned in 8 minutes

     A) $\dfrac{\$18.3}{\text{minute}}$

     B) $\dfrac{18.3 \text{ minutes}}{\$1}$

     C) $\dfrac{\$146.40}{8 \text{ minutes}}$

     D) $\dfrac{146.40 \text{ minutes}}{\$8}$

     E) $\dfrac{109.80 \text{ minutes}}{\$6}$

40. Determine whether the proportion is true or false.
     $\dfrac{10 \text{ rolls}}{15 \text{ feet}} = \dfrac{5 \text{ rolls}}{6 \text{ feet}}$

     A) True
     B) False

Sample Test
Prepared by Houghton Mifflin

Answer Key

1. A
2. A
3. B
4. D
5. A
6. E
7. C
8. A
9. A
10. D
11. A
12. B
13. A
14. A
15. B
16. E
17. C
18. A
19. B
20. C
21. A
22. B
23. A
24. B
25. C
26. D
27. E
28. A
29. B
30. D
31. C
32. B
33. A
34. A
35. B
36. E
37. A
38. D
39. A
40. B

Sample Test
Prepared by Houghton Mifflin

Sample Test
Prepared by Houghton Mifflin

Name: _____ Date: _____

1. 12.5% of what is 40?
   A) 12.5
   B) 40
   C) 320
   D) 4
   E) 125

2. Funtimes Amusement Park has 550 employees and must hire an additional 18% for the vacation season. What is the total number of employees needed for the vacation season?
   A) 649
   B) 451
   C) 99
   D) 149
   E) 501

3. What is 30% of 26.25?
   A) 7.875
   B) 78.75
   C) 11.429
   D) 1.143
   E) 787.5

4. Write $2\frac{7}{9}$ as a percent. Write the remainder (if there is a remainder) in fractional form.
   A) $177\frac{7}{9}\%$
   B) $277\frac{7}{9}\%$
   C) $377\frac{8}{9}\%$
   D) $177\frac{8}{9}\%$
   E) None of the above.

Sample Test
Prepared by Houghton Mifflin

5. What percent of 200 is 224?
   A) 112%
   B) 224%
   C) 200%
   D) 100%
   E) 2800%

6. What percent of 200 is 14?
   A) 350%
   B) 14%
   C) 200%
   D) 100%
   E) 7%

7. In a survey, people were asked how they planned to use their tax refunds. 300 people, or 6% of the respondents, said they would save the money. How many people responded to the survey?
   A) 6
   B) 300
   C) 5000
   D) 100
   E) 150

8. A sales tax of 14% of the cost of a car was added to the purchase price of $24,000.
   a. How much was the sales tax?
   b. What is the total cost of the car, including sales tax?
   A) a) $3370.00; b) $27,370.00
   B) a) $3360.00; b) $27,360.00
   C) a) $3365.00; b) $27,365.00
   D) a) $3360.00; b) $20,640.00
   E) a) $3370.00; b) $20,630.00

9. Suppose that 58 billion pounds of a product were produced in the United States last year, of which 19 billion pounds were wasted. What percent of production was wasted? Round to the nearest tenth of a percent.
   A) 19.0%
   B) 3.3%
   C) 32.8%
   D) 1.9%
   E) 58.0%

Sample Test
Prepared by Houghton Mifflin

10. Write 2.4% as a decimal.
    A) 0.24
    B) 24
    C) 2.4
    D) 0.024
    E) 240

11. What is 44% of 93?
    A) 4092
    B) 409.2
    C) 4.73
    D) 0.47
    E) 40.92

12. What percent of 8 is 1.2?
    A) 12%
    B) 1.2%
    C) 8%
    D) 15%
    E) 1.5%

13. 15.6 is what percent of 6?
    A) 6%
    B) 15.6%
    C) 260%
    D) 156%
    E) 26%

14. What is 0.26% of 597?
    A) 15.522
    B) 1.5522
    C) 0.0044
    D) 0.0004
    E) 155.22

15. Write 0.3 as a percent.
    A) 30 %
    B) 300 %
    C) 0.3 %
    D) 0.03 %
    E) 0.003 %

Sample Test
Prepared by Houghton Mifflin

16. Which is larger: 4% of 90, or 75% of 6?
    A) 75% of 6
    B) 4% of 90
    C) The two amounts are equal.

17. 45% of what is 13.5?
    A) 45
    B) 13.5
    C) 30
    D) 100
    E) 90

18. What is $12\frac{1}{2}$% of 1440?
    A) 170
    B) 80
    C) 180
    D) 230
    E) 200

19. Write 0.264 as a percent.
    A) 2.64 %
    B) 26.4 %
    C) 0.264 %
    D) 264 %
    E) 2640 %

20. Write $\frac{1}{7}$ as a percent. Round to the nearest tenth of a percent, if necessary.
    A) 71.5 %
    B) 14.3 %
    C) 0.1 %
    D) 7.1 %
    E) 0.7 %

Sample Test
Prepared by Houghton Mifflin

21. During the packaging process for oranges, an inspector discards spoiled oranges. On a given day, an inspector found that 4% of the 30,000 pounds of oranges were spoiled.
    a. How many pounds of oranges were spoiled?
    b. How many pounds of oranges were not spoiled?
    A) a) 1200; b) 28,800
    B) a) 1090; b) 28,910
    C) a) 1700; b) 31,700
    D) a) 1200; b) 31,200
    E) a) 1090; b) 31,090

22. Write $\dfrac{2}{7}$ as a percent. Round to the nearest tenth of a percent, if necessary.
    A) 142.9 %
    B) 28.6 %
    C) 285.7 %
    D) 5.7 %
    E) 0.6 %

23. What is 275% of 40?
    A) 125
    B) 100
    C) 115
    D) 120
    E) 110

24. 98 is $6\dfrac{1}{4}$ % of what?
    A) 6
    B) 7
    C) 1568
    D) 1566
    E) 1567

25. In a test of the breaking strength of concrete slabs for freeway construction, 2 of the 200 slabs tested did not meet safety requirements. What percent of the slabs did meet safety requirements?
    A) 99 %
    B) 99.9 %
    C) 1 %
    D) 0.1 %
    E) 100 %

Sample Test
Prepared by Houghton Mifflin

26. Write $\dfrac{9}{25}$ as a percent. Write the remainder (if there is a remainder) in fractional form.
   A) 90 %
   B) 9 %
   C) 360 %
   D) 36 %
   E) 900 %

27. Write $\dfrac{19}{25}$ as a percent.
   A) 760 %
   B) 19 %
   C) 76 %
   D) 190 %
   E) 0.76 %

28. Write $4\dfrac{1}{2}\%$ as a fraction.
   A) $\dfrac{3}{100}$
   B) $\dfrac{9}{400}$
   C) $\dfrac{9}{100}$
   D) $\dfrac{9}{200}$
   E) None of the above.

29. Write 1.252 as a percent.
   A) 125.2 %
   B) 12.52 %
   C) 1.252 %
   D) 0.01252 %
   E) 0.1252 %

Sample Test
Prepared by Houghton Mifflin

30. Suppose that 24.4% of the women and 26.5% of the men in a country today have earned a bachelor's or graduate degree. How many men in the country have earned a bachelor's or graduate degree?
    A) 2,440,000,000
    B) 1,220,000,000
    C) 2,650,000,000
    D) 1,325,000,000
    E) Insufficient information

31. Write $3\frac{1}{4}$ as a percent. Round to the nearest tenth of a percent, if necessary.
    A) 225 %
    B) 325 %
    C) 32.5 %
    D) 22.5 %
    E) 11.3 %

32. During a quality control test, Micronics found that 35 computer motherboards were defective. This amount was 0.7% of the computer boards tested.
    a. How many computer boards were tested?
    b. How many computer boards tested were not defective?
    A) a) 5000; b) 4965
    B) a) 50; b) 15
    C) a) 500; b) 535
    D) a) 5000; b) 5035
    E) a) 50; b) 85

33. 108 is 216% of what?
    A) 216
    B) 108
    C) 50
    D) 100
    E) 1350

34. What is 74.4% of 605?
    A) 449.115
    B) 449.11
    C) 451.125
    D) 450.12
    E) 451.14

35. Which is smaller: 70% of 16, or 14% of 95?
    A) 70% of 16
    B) 14% of 95
    C) The two amounts are equal.

36. Write 6.95 as a percent.
    A) 695 %
    B) 69.5 %
    C) 6.95 %
    D) 6950 %
    E) 0.695 %

37. Write 96% as a fraction and as a decimal.
    A) $\dfrac{24}{25}$; 96
    B) $\dfrac{24}{25}$; 0.96
    C) $\dfrac{48}{5}$; 96
    D) $\dfrac{48}{5}$; 9.6
    E) $\dfrac{24}{25}$; 9600

38. Write $\dfrac{3}{35}$ as a percent. Write the remainder (if there is a remainder) in fractional form.
    A) $6\dfrac{41}{70}$ %
    B) $7\dfrac{4}{7}$ %
    C) $8\dfrac{4}{7}$ %
    D) $7\dfrac{41}{70}$ %
    E) None of the above.

Sample Test
Prepared by Houghton Mifflin

39. Suppose that three in four couples disagree on a particular matter. What percent of couples disagree on the matter?
    A) 75%
    B) 7.5%
    C) 3%
    D) 12%
    E) 1.2%

40. What is 0.4% of 2000?
    A) 11
    B) 7
    C) 9
    D) 10
    E) 8

Sample Test
Prepared by Houghton Mifflin

Answer Key

1. C
2. A
3. A
4. B
5. A
6. E
7. C
8. B
9. C
10. D
11. E
12. D
13. C
14. B
15. A
16. A
17. C
18. C
19. B
20. B
21. A
22. B
23. E
24. C
25. A
26. D
27. C
28. D
29. A
30. E
31. B
32. A
33. C
34. D
35. A
36. A
37. B
38. C
39. A
40. E

Sample Test
Prepared by Houghton Mifflin

Name: _____ Date: _____

1. The number of big-screen televisions sold each month for 1 year was recorded by an electronics store. The results were 16, 13, 25, 25, 22, 19, 26, 27, 19, 25, 16, and 31. Calculate the mean, the median, and the mode of the number of televisions sold per month.
   A) Mean: 22 TVs; median: 23.5 TVs; mode: 25 TVs
   B) Mean: 22 TVs; median: 25 TVs; mode: 23.5 TVs
   C) Mean: 23.5 TVs; median: 23.5 TVs; mode: 25 TVs
   D) Mean: 22 TVs; median: 22 TVs; mode: 23.5 TVs
   E) Mean: 23.5 TVs; median: 25 TVs; mode: 22 TVs

2. The number of seats occupied per flight on a jet for 16 trans-Atlantic flights was recorded. The numbers were 311, 447, 397, 435, 414, 359, 371, 321, 428, 401, 335, 424, 411, 392, 432, and 410. Calculate the mean, the median, and the mode of the number of seats occupied per flight.
   A) Mean: 393 seats; median: 405.5 seats; mode: no mode
   B) Mean: 393 seats; median: 399.25 seats; mode: 405.5 seats
   C) Mean: 405.5 seats; median: 405.5 seats; mode: 399.25 seats
   D) Mean: 399.25 seats; median: 405.5 seats; mode: no mode
   E) Mean: 399.25 seats; median: 405.5 seats; mode: 393 seats

3. The times, in seconds, for a 100-meter dash at a college track meet were 11.06, 10.80, 11.19, 11.62, 10.83, 11.47, 11.31, 11.24, 11.15, and 11.34.
   a. Calculate the mean time for the 100-meter dash.
   b. Calculate the median time for the 100-meter dash.
   A) (a) Mean: 11.201 seconds; (b) median: 11.201 seconds
   B) (a) Mean: 11.201 seconds; (b) median: 11.215 seconds
   C) (a) Mean: 11.215 seconds; (b) median: 11.215 seconds
   D) (a) Mean: 11.215 seconds; (b) median: 11.201 seconds
   E) None of the above

4. A consumer research group purchased identical items in eight grocery stores. The costs for the purchased items were $44.29, $50.68, $39.84, $39.11, $47.26, $40.83, $46.31, and $44.23. Calculate the mean and the median costs of the purchased items. Round your answers to three decimal places.
   A) Mean: $44.260; median: $44.260
   B) Mean: $44.069; median: $44.260
   C) Mean: $44.069; median: $44.069
   D) Mean: $44.260; median: $44.069
   E) None of the above

Sample Test
Prepared by Houghton Mifflin

5. Eight health maintenance organizations (HMOs) presented group health insurance plans to a company. The monthly rates per employee were $414, $385, $396, $389, $419, $355, $392, and $426. Calculate the mean and the median monthly rates for these eight HMOs.

   A) Mean: $394; median: $394
   B) Mean: $397; median: $394
   C) Mean: $397; median: $397
   D) Mean: $394; median: $397
   E) None of the above

6. The box-and-whiskers plot below shows the distribution of median incomes for 50 towns. What is the lowest value in the set of data? The highest value? The first quartile? The third quartile? The median? Find the range and the interquartile range.

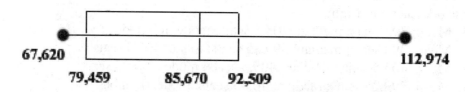

67,620   79,459   85,670   92,509   112,974

   A) Lowest = $67,620; highest = $112,974; Q_1 = $92,509; Q_3 = $79,459; median = $85,670; range = $45,354; interquartile range = $13,050
   B) Lowest = $67,620; highest = $112,974; Q_1 = $79,459; Q_3 = $92,509; median = $85,670; range = $13,050; interquartile range = $45,354
   C) Lowest = $67,620; highest = $112,974; Q_1 = $79,459; Q_3 = $92,509; median = $85,670; range = $45,354; interquartile range = $13,050
   D) Lowest = $67,620; highest = $112,974; Q_1 = $92,509; Q_3 = $79,459; median = $85,670; range = $13,050; interquartile range = $45,354
   E) None of the above

Sample Test
Prepared by Houghton Mifflin

7. The cholesterol levels for 80 adults were recorded and then displayed in the box-and-whiskers plot shown below.
   a. How many adults had a cholesterol level above 212?
   b. How many adults had a cholesterol level below 249?
   c. How many cholesterol levels are represented in each quartile?
   d. What percent of the adults had a cholesterol level of not more than 193?

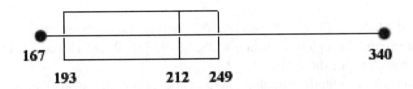

 167   340

  193   212 249

A) (a) 40 adults; (b) 60 adults; (c) 20 cholesterol levels; (d) 25%
B) (a) 40 adults; (b) 20 adults; (c) 60 cholesterol levels; (d) 75%
C) (a) 20 adults; (b) 60 adults; (c) 40 cholesterol levels; (d) 75%
D) (a) 20 adults; (b) 60 adults; (c) 40 cholesterol levels; (d) 25%
E) None of the above

8. The prices per ounce in cents of ten shampoos sold at the market are 11, 54, 27, 31, 69, 15, 57, 63, 31 and 72. Find the mean, median and mode of the prices per ounce.
   A) Mean: 42.5 cents; median: 43 cents; mode: 31 cents
   B) Mean: 31 cents; median: 43 cents; mode: 42.5 cents
   C) Mean: 43 cents; median: 42.5 cents; mode: 31 cents
   D) Mean: 31 cents; median: 42.5 cents; mode: 43 cents
   E) None of the above

Sample Test
Prepared by Houghton Mifflin

9. The heights of ten varsity basketball players at Mountain View College were measured in inches and found to be 74, 82, 78, 72, 78, 73, 78, 72, 78 and 81. Find the mean, median and mode of the heights.
   A) Mean: 78 inches; median: 78 inches; mode: 76.6 inches
   B) Mean: 78 inches; median: 76.6 inches; mode: 76.6 inches
   C) Mean: 78 inches; median: 76.6 inches; mode: 78 inches
   D) Mean: 76.6 inches; median: 78 inches; mode: 78 inches
   E) None of the above

10. Statistical Abstracts (117th edition) reports gasoline excise taxes, in cents per gallon, in the west (mountain region) as follows: 28, 26, 9, 22, 19, 18, 19 and 24. Find the mean, median and mode of these taxes.
   A) Mean: 19 cents/gallon; median: 20.5 cents/gallon: 20.6 cents/gallon
   B) Mean: 20.5 cents/gallon; median: 20.6 cents/gallon; mode: 19 cents/gallon
   C) Mean: 20.6 cents/gallon; median: 19 cents/gallon; mode: 20.5 cents/gallon
   D) Mean: 20.6 cents/gallon; median: 20.5 cents/gallon; mode: 19 cents/gallon
   E) None of the above

11. In an effort to estimate the size of elk herds wintering in the Rocky Mountain National Park, the rangers used a small airplane to spot count groups of elk in the Park. They found 15 groups of elk and recorded the size of each group as: 21, 15, 19, 16, 18, 17, 17, 20, 25, 7, 16, 10, 16, 18 and 12. Compute the mean, the median and the mode of the data.
   A) Mean: 17 elks; median: 17 elks; mode: 16 elks
   B) Mean: 17 elks; median: 16 elks; mode: 16.5 elks
   C) Mean: 16 elks; median: 16.5 elks; mode: 17 elks
   D) Mean: 16.5 elks; median: 16 elks; mode: 17 elks
   E) None of the above

12. Statistical Abstracts (117th edition) reports average travel time to work for commuters in the New England states to be (to the nearest minute): 19, 22, 18, 23, 19 and 21. Find the mean, median and mode of these commuting times.
   A) Mean: 20.3 minutes; median: 19 minutes; mode: 20 minutes
   B) Mean: 19 minutes; median: 20 minutes; mode: 20.3 minutes
   C) Mean: 19 minutes; median: 20.3 minutes; mode: 20 minutes
   D) Mean: 20.3 minutes; median: 20 minutes; mode: 19 minutes
   E) None of the above

Sample Test
Prepared by Houghton Mifflin

13. Find the mean of the following ages of retirees: 79, 75, 83, 91, 66, 68, 72, 81, 64, 68, 71, 66, 86, 64, 80, 69, 66 and 65.
    A) 66 years
    B) 68.5 years
    C) 72 years
    D) 73 years
    E) 70 years

14. Petroleum pollution in oceans is known to increase the growth of a certain bacteria. Brian did a project for his ecology class in which he made a bacteria count (per 100 millimeters) in nine random samples of seawater. His counts gave the following readings: 17, 23, 18, 19, 21, 16, 12, 15 and 18. Find the sample mean.
    A) 17.59 bacteria per 100 millimeters
    B) 17.95 bacteria per 100 millimeters
    C) 17.67 bacteria per 100 millimeters
    D) 17.83 bacteria per 100 millimeters
    E) 17.76 bacteria per 100 millimeters

15. In the process of tuna fishing, porpoises are sometimes accidentally caught and killed. A U.S. oceanographic institute wants to study the number of porpoises killed in this way. Records from eight commercial tuna fishing fleets gave the following information about the number of porpoises killed in a three-month period: 2, 6, 18, 9, 0, 15, 3 and 10. Find the sample mean.
    A) 7.23 porpoises
    B) 7.88 porpoises
    C) 7.65 porpoises
    D) 7.72 porpoises
    E) 7.41 porpoises

16. A swimmer was timed while swimming across a small lake six times. Find the median of her six times (min:sec): 3:20, 3:08, 2:51, 3:31, 2:49 and 2:56.
    A) 3:00
    B) 3:02
    C) 3:08
    D) 2:58
    E) 3:06

Sample Test
Prepared by Houghton Mifflin

17. Response time for eight emergency phone calls in a large metropolitan area were measured to the nearest minute and found to be: 7, 10, 8, 5, 8, 6, 8 and 9. Find the mean, the median and the mode of the response times.
    A) Mean: 7.63 minutes; median: 8 minutes; mode: 8 minutes
    B) Mean: 8 minutes; median: 8 minutes; mode: 7.63 minutes
    C) Mean: 8 minutes; median: 7.63 minutes; mode: 8 minutes
    D) Mean: 8 minutes; median: 7.63 minutes; mode: 7.63 minutes
    E) None of the above

18. Find the mode of the following set of numbers: 1, 4, 3, 2, 2, 1, 3, 3, 4, 1, 2, 4, 4, 1, 2 and 3.
    A) 2.5
    B) 4
    C) No mode
    D) 3
    E) 2

19. City Hospital has a temporary shortage of nurses, so nurses have been working overtime. A random sample of six nurses reported that the number of overtime hours they worked last week were: 7, 2, 4, 5, 4 and 3. Find the mean, the median and the mode of this data set.
    A) Mean: 4 hours; median: 4 hours; mode: 4 hours
    B) Mean: 4.17; median: 4.17 hours; mode: 4 hours
    C) Mean: 4.17; median: 4 hours; mode: 4.17 hours
    D) Mean: 4 hours; median: 4 hours; mode: 4.17 hours
    E) None of the above

20. Find the mean of the following credit card interest rates (%): 7.9, 11.9, 24.5, 21.1, 15.9 and 9.9.
    A) 15%
    B) 15.2%
    C) 15.4%
    D) 15.8%
    E) 16.0%

Sample Test
Prepared by Houghton Mifflin

Answer Key

1. A
2. A
3. B
4. B
5. B
6. C
7. A
8. C
9. D
10. D
11. E
12. D
13. D
14. C
15. B
16. B
17. A
18. C
19. E
20. B

Sample Test
Prepared by Houghton Mifflin

Sample Test
Prepared by Houghton Mifflin

Name: _____ Date: _____

1. Evaluate the variable expression when $a = -8$, $b = 9$, $c = -4$, and $d = 4$.

$$\frac{b + 6d}{b}$$

A) $\dfrac{1}{3}$

B) $\dfrac{1}{11}$

C) 1

D) $\dfrac{11}{3}$

E) Undefined

2. Evaluate the variable expression when $a = 2$, $b = 5$, and $c = -4$.

$$a^2 - \frac{ac}{8}$$

A) -5

B) 3

C) 5

D) 10

E) 8

3. Evaluate the variable expression when $a = -4$, $b = 3$, $c = -7$, and $d = 8$.

$$\frac{b^2 - a}{ad + 3c}$$

A) $\dfrac{1}{53}$

B) $\dfrac{1}{3}$

C) 1

D) $-\dfrac{13}{53}$

E) Undefined

4. Evaluate the variable expression when $a = -6$, $b = 5$, $c = -8$, and $d = 3$.

$(b + c)^2 - 3a$
A) -27
B) 27
C) -9
D) 54
E) -24

5. Evaluate the variable expression when $a = 2$, $b = 3$, and $c = -6$.

$c - (c + a)^2$
A) -16
B) -23
C) -22
D) -44
E) -19

6. Evaluate the variable expression when $a = -6$, $b = 5$, $c = -6$, and $d = 8$.

$$\frac{b^2 - c}{ad + 5c}$$
A) $\dfrac{1}{78}$
B) $\dfrac{1}{5}$
C) 1
D) $-\dfrac{31}{78}$
E) Undefined

7. The value of z is the value of $a^2 - 2a$ when $a = -6$. Find the value of z^2.
A) 2306
B) 0
C) 2300
D) 48
E) 2304

8. Evaluate the variable expression when $a = 5$, $b = 9$, and $c = -5$.

   $b^2 - c^2$
   A) -56
   B) 53
   C) 56
   D) 112
   E) 59

9. Evaluate the variable expression when $a = 5$, $b = 7$, and $c = -5$.

   $c^2 - 4ac$
   A) 0
   B) -75
   C) -51
   D) -105
   E) 125

10. The value of z is the value of $a^2 - 4a$ when $a = -12$. Find the value of z^2.
    A) 36866
    B) 0
    C) 36863
    D) 192
    E) 36864

11. Evaluate the variable expression when $a = 7$, $b = 10$, and $c = -9$.

    $-3a + 4c$
    A) 19
    B) -57
    C) 15
    D) -21
    E) -55

12. The value of a is the value of $5x^2 - 5x - 5$ when $x = -1$. Find the value of $5a - 5$.
    A) 20
    B) 30
    C) 15
    D) -20
    E) 21

Sample Test
Prepared by Houghton Mifflin

13. Evaluate the variable expression when $a = 9$, $b = 6$, and $c = -10$.

$a^2 - b^2$
A) -45
B) 42
C) 45
D) 90
E) 47

14. Evaluate the variable expression when $a = 4$, $b = 2$, and $c = -3$.

$a - (a + b)^2$
A) -28
B) -34
C) -32
D) -64
E) -31

15. Evaluate the variable expression when $a = -10$, $b = 2$, $c = -12$, and $d = 5$.

$(b + c)^2 - 5a$
A) -150
B) 150
C) 50
D) 300
E) -148

16. Evaluate the variable expression when $a = 4$, $b = 3$, and $c = -4$.

$c^2 - \dfrac{ac}{8}$
A) -18
B) 17
C) 18
D) 36
E) 20

Sample Test
Prepared by Houghton Mifflin

17. Evaluate the variable expression when $a = -5$, $b = 5$, $c = -12$, and $d = 4$.

$$\frac{b + 6d}{b}$$

A) $\dfrac{1}{5}$

B) $\dfrac{1}{29}$

C) 1

D) $\dfrac{29}{5}$

E) Undefined

18. Evaluate the variable expression when $a = 8$, $b = 9$, and $c = -10$.

$c^2 - 4ac$

A) 20
B) −220
C) −239
D) −330
E) 420

19. The value of a is the value of $5x^2 - 4x - 5$ when $x = -4$. Find the value of $4a - 5$.
A) 359
B) 369
C) 100
D) -15
E) 360

20. Evaluate the variable expression when $a = 3$, $b = 9$, and $c = -5$.

$-3a + 4b$
A) −29
B) 27
C) −45
D) −9
E) 28

Sample Test
Prepared by Houghton Mifflin

Answer Key

1. D
2. C
3. D
4. B
5. C
6. D
7. E
8. C
9. E
10. E
11. B
12. A
13. C
14. C
15. B
16. C
17. D
18. E
19. A
20. B

Sample Test
Prepared by Houghton Mifflin

Name: _____ Date: _____

1. Translate the following into a variable expression.

   the sum of five-sixths of x and 6

   A) $\dfrac{5}{6}x+6$

   B) $\dfrac{5}{6}(x+6)$

   C) $\dfrac{6}{5}x+6$

   D) $5x+6$

   E) $\dfrac{5}{6}x-6$

2. Translate the following into a variable expression.

   7 less than the product of z and -5

   A) $7(z-5)$

   B) $5z-7$

   C) $7-5z$

   D) $-5z-7$

   E) $5-7z$

3. Translate the following into a variable expression.

   The product of 6 and the total of p and 3

   A) $6(p+3)$

   B) $6p+3$

   C) $p(6+3)$

   D) $3(p+6)$

   E) $6(p-3)$

Sample Test
Prepared by Houghton Mifflin

4. Translate the following into a variable expression.

   10 divided by the difference between z and 3
   A) $\dfrac{3}{z-10}$
   B) $\dfrac{10}{3-z}$
   C) $\dfrac{10}{z}-3$
   D) $\dfrac{10}{z-3}$
   E) $\dfrac{10}{z\div 3}$

5. Translate the following into a variable expression.

   5 times the difference between y and 10
   A) $10(y-5)$
   B) $5(y+10)$
   C) $5(10-y)$
   D) $5y-10$
   E) $5(y-10)$

6. Translate the following into a variable expression.

   The sum of z and 6
   A) $z-6$
   B) $6z$
   C) $z+6$
   D) $\dfrac{z}{6}$
   E) $z\div 6$

Sample Test
Prepared by Houghton Mifflin

7. Translate the following into a variable expression.

The ratio of 7 more than p to p

A) $\dfrac{7+p}{p}$

B) $\dfrac{p}{p+7}$

C) $\dfrac{7}{p}+p$

D) $\dfrac{7-p}{p}$

E) $\dfrac{p}{7-p}$

8. Translate the following into a variable expression.

The total of 8 times the cube of x and 10 times the square of x

A) $8x^3 \div 10x^2$

B) $8x^3 + 10x^2$

C) $8x^2 + 10x^3$

D) $8^3 x + 10^2 x$

E) $8x^3 - 10x^2$

9. Translate the following into a variable expression.

Ten less than the product of a number and four

A) $4 - 10a$

B) $10 - 4a$

C) $10a - 4$

D) $4a - 10$

E) $10 + 4a$

Sample Test
Prepared by Houghton Mifflin

10. In 1951, phone companies began using area codes. According to information found at
    www.area-codes.com, at the beginning of 2004 there were 205 more area codes than
    there were in 1951.

    Express the number of area codes in 2004 in terms of the number of area codes in 1951.
    A) Number of area codes in 1951: A Number of area codes in 2004: $A + 205$
    B) Number of area codes in 1951: A Number of area codes in 2004: $A - 205$
    C) Number of area codes in 1951: $A + 205$ Number of area codes in 2004: A
    D) Number of area codes in 1951: A Number of area codes in 2004: 205
    E) Number of area codes in 1951: 205   Number of area codes in 2004: A

11. Translate the following into a variable expression.

    x decreased by the product of 3 and x
    A) $3x$
    B) $x - 3x$
    C) $x - 3$
    D) $3x - x$
    E) $x + 3x$

12. Translate the following into a variable expression.

    y multiplied by 6
    A) $y + 6$
    B) $6y$
    C) $y - 6$
    D) $\dfrac{y}{6}$
    E) $6 - y$

Sample Test
Prepared by Houghton Mifflin

13. Translate the following into a variable expression.

Five minus a number
A) $5 - p$
B) $5p$
C) $p - 5$
D) $\dfrac{p}{5}$
E) $p \div 5$

14. A halyard 14 ft long was cut into two pieces of different lengths.

Use one variable to express the lengths of the two pieces.
A) Length of one piece: H Length of second piece: $H + 14$
B) Length of one piece: H Length of second piece: $14 - H$
C) Length of one piece: $H + 14$ Length of second piece: H
D) Length of one piece: H Length of second piece: 14
E) Length of one piece: 14   Length of second piece: H

15. Translate the following into a variable expression.

y increased by 5
A) $y - 5$
B) $5y$
C) $y + 5$
D) $\dfrac{y}{5}$
E) $5 - y$

Sample Test
Prepared by Houghton Mifflin

16. Translate the following into a variable expression.

    The quotient of twice a number and five
    A) $\dfrac{2+a}{5}$

    B) $\dfrac{2}{5}+a$

    C) $2+\dfrac{a}{5}$

    D) $\dfrac{2a}{5}$

    E) $\dfrac{5a}{2}$

17. Translate the following into a variable expression.

    7 less than p
    A) $p-7$
    B) $7p$
    C) $p+7$
    D) $\dfrac{p}{7}$
    E) $7-p$

18. Translate the following into a variable expression.

    z decreased by 5
    A) $z+5$
    B) $5z$
    C) $z-5$
    D) $\dfrac{z}{5}$
    E) $5-z$

Sample Test
Prepared by Houghton Mifflin

19. Translate the following into a variable expression.

   z added to 6
   A) $z - 6$
   B) $6z$
   C) $6 + z$
   D) $\dfrac{z}{6}$
   E) $6 - z$

20. Translate the following into a variable expression.

   A number divided by twelve
   A) $z - 12$
   B) $12z$
   C) $z + 12$
   D) $\dfrac{z}{12}$
   E) $12 - z$

Sample Test
Prepared by Houghton Mifflin

Answer Key

1. A
2. D
3. A
4. D
5. E
6. C
7. A
8. B
9. D
10. A
11. B
12. B
13. A
14. B
15. C
16. D
17. A
18. C
19. C
20. D

Sample Test
Prepared by Houghton Mifflin

Name: _____ Date: _____

1. Expand:

$$(3z+5)^2$$

A) $9z^2 - 25$
B) $9z^2 + 30z + 25$
C) $9z^2 - 30z + 25$
D) $9z^2 - 30z - 25$
E) $9z^2 + 25$

2. Multiply:

$$(2z^2 - 2z + 1)(-2z^3)$$

A) $-4z^5 + 4z^4 + 2z^3$
B) $-4z^5 - 4z^4 + 2z^3$
C) $-4z^5 + 4z^4 - 2z^3$
D) $4z^5 - 4z^4 - 2z^3$
E) $4z^4 - 4z^5 + 2z^3$

3. State whether the expression below is a monomial, a binomial, a trinomial, or none of these.

$3x^2 - 6x - 3$
A) Monomial
B) Binomial
C) Trinomial
D) None of these

4. Multiply:

$$2x^3(-6x^2 - 5x + 1)$$

A) $-12x^5 - 10x^4 - 2x^3$
B) $-12x^5 - 10x^4 + 2x^3$
C) $-12x^5 - 10x + 2$
D) $-12x^5 + 10x^4 + 2x^3$
E) $-12x^4 - 10x^5 + 2x^3$

Sample Test
Prepared by Houghton Mifflin

5. Divide:

$$\frac{7a^8 - 2a^6}{-a^4}$$

A) $-7a^4 + 2a^2$

B) $7a^2 + 2a^4$

C) $-7a^4 - 2a^2$

D) $-7a^8 + 2a^2$

E) $7a^4 - 2a^2$

6. Divide:

$$\frac{t^3 - 8t^2 + 21t - 20}{t - 4}$$

A) $t^2 + 4t + 5$

B) $t^2 - 4t + 5$

C) $t^2 - 4t - 5$

D) $t^2 - 5t + 4$

E) $-t^2 + 4t + 5$

7. Add the following. Use a horizontal format.

$$\left(2y^3 - 6y^2 + 9y\right) + \left(-16 - 5y + 3y^2\right)$$

A) $2y^3 + 3y^2 + 4y - 16$

B) $2y^3 - 3y^2 + 4y + 16$

C) $2y^3 - 3y^2 + 4y - 16$

D) $2y^3 - 3y^2 - 4y - 16$

E) $2y^3 - 3y^2 + 4y - 3$

Sample Test
Prepared by Houghton Mifflin

8. Multiply:

$$\left(y^3 + 2y^2 - 2y + 1\right)\left(y + 5\right)$$

A) $y^4 + 7y^3 + 8y^2 + 9y + 5$

B) $y^4 - 7y^3 + 8y^2 - 9y + 5$

C) $y^4 + 7y^3 - 9y + 5$

D) $y^4 + 7y^3 + 8y^2 - 9y + 5$

E) $y^4 + 7y^3 - 8y^2 - 9y - 5$

9. Divide:

$$\frac{3c^5 - 3c^8 - 4c^{10}}{c^2}$$

A) $3c^3 - 3c^8 - 4c^8$

B) $3c^3 - 3c^6 - 4c^{10}$

C) $3c^3 - 3c^6 - 4c^8$

D) $3c^3 - 3c^8 - 4c^6$

E) $3c^3 - 3c^8 - 4c^{10}$

10. Divide:

$$\frac{12t^2x^2 + 36xt}{xt}$$

A) $12tx + 36$

B) $12tx + \dfrac{36}{tx}$

C) $12tx - 36$

D) $12 + 36xt$

E) $\dfrac{12}{tx} + 36$

Sample Test
Prepared by Houghton Mifflin

11. Multiply:

$$ab\left(5a^2 - 5ab + 8b^2\right)$$

  A) $5a^3b - 5a^2b^2 + 8ab^2$

  B) $5a^3b - 5a^2b + 8ab^3$

  C) $5a^3b + 5a^2b^2 + 8ab^3$

  D) $5a^3b - 5a^2b^2 + 8a^3b$

  E) $5a^3b - 5a^2b^2 + 8ab^3$

12. Add the following. Use a vertical format.

$$\left(3x^2 + 2x + 5\right) + \left(3x^2 + 6x - 8\right)$$

  A) $6x^2 + 2x - 3$

  B) $6x^2 + 8x + 3$

  C) $6x + 8x^2 - 3$

  D) $6x^2 + 8x - 3$

  E) $6x^2 + 8x - 5$

13. Divide:

$$\frac{8y^2 - 6y - 3}{4y + 3}$$

  A) $2y + 3 - \dfrac{6}{4y + 3}$

  B) $2y + 3 + \dfrac{1}{4y + 3}$

  C) $2y - 3 + \dfrac{6}{4y + 3}$

  D) $2y^2 + 3 + \dfrac{6}{4y + 3}$

  E) $2 + 3y + \dfrac{6}{4y + 3}$

Sample Test
Prepared by Houghton Mifflin

14. Multiply:

$$\left(x^2 - 7x + 5\right)\left(2x - 3\right)$$

A) $2x^3 - 17x^2 + 31x - 15$
B) $2x^3 - 17x^2 + 31x + 15$
C) $2x^3 - 17x^2 - 31x - 15$
D) $2x^3 + 17x^2 + 31x - 15$
E) $2x^3 + 17x^2 - 31x - 15$

15. State whether the expression below is a monomial.

$$\frac{8x}{17y}$$

A) No
B) Yes

16. Divide:

$$\left(y^2 - 10y + 21\right) \div \left(y - 3\right)$$

A) $y + 7$
B) $y - 7$
C) $y^2 - 7$
D) $y + 3$
E) $y + 10$

Sample Test
Prepared by Houghton Mifflin

17. Divide:

$$\left(4t^2 + 16t + 21\right) \div \left(2t + 5\right)$$

A) $2t + 3 - \dfrac{6}{2t+5}$

B) $2t + 3 + \dfrac{6}{2t+5}$

C) $2t - 3 + \dfrac{6}{2t+5}$

D) $2t^2 + 3 + \dfrac{6}{2t+5}$

E) $2 + 3t + \dfrac{6}{2t+5}$

18. Expand:

$$\left(x - 5\right)^2$$

A) $x^2 - 25$

B) $x^2 - 10x + 25$

C) $x^2 + 10x + 25$

D) $x^2 - 10x - 25$

E) $x^2 + 25$

19. Add the following. Use a vertical format.

$$\left(2r^3 - 8r^2 + 9r\right) + \left(-16 - 4r + 3r^2\right)$$

A) $2r^3 + 5r^2 + 5r - 16$

B) $2r^3 - 5r^2 + 5r + 16$

C) $2r^3 - 5r^2 + 5r - 16$

D) $2r^3 - 5r^2 - 5r - 16$

E) $2r^3 - 5r^2 + 5r - 3$

Sample Test
Prepared by Houghton Mifflin

20. Divide:

$$\frac{5x^{12} - 3x^{10} - 4x^7}{x^4}$$

A) $5x^8 - 3x^{10} - 4x^7$
B) $5x^{12} - 3x^{10} - 4x^3$
C) $5x^8 - 3x^6 - 4x^3$
D) $5x^8 - 3x^{10} - 4x^3$
E) $5x^{12} - 3x^6 - 4x^7$

21. Subtract the following. Use a vertical format.

$$\left(4y^2 - 7y + 7\right) - \left(-10 + 4y - 3y^3\right)$$

A) $3y^3 + 4y^2 + 11y - 17$
B) $3y^3 - 4y^2 + 11y + 17$
C) $3y^3 + 4y^2 - 11y + 17$
D) $3y^3 - 4y^2 - 11y - 17$
E) $3y^3 - 4y^2 + 11y + 3$

22. Subtract the following. Use a horizontal format.

$$\left(5x^3 + 11x + 8\right) - \left(-11x^2 + 5x - 3\right)$$

A) $5x^3 - 11x^2 - 6x + 11$
B) $5x^3 - 11x^2 + 6x + 11$
C) $5x^3 + 11x^2 + 6x + 11$
D) $5x^3 - 11x^2 - 6x - 11$
E) $5x^3 - 11x^2 + 6x - 3$

23. The radius of a circle is $(4x+2)$ cm.

Find the area of the circle in terms of the variable x. Leave the answer in terms of π.
A) $16\pi x^2 - 16\pi x + 4\pi$ cm^2
B) $16\pi x^2 + 16x + 4\pi$ cm^2
C) $16\pi x^2 + 16\pi x + 4\pi$ cm^2
D) $16\pi x^2 + 4\pi$ cm^2
E) $16\pi x^2 + 16\pi x + 4\pi$ cm

Sample Test
Prepared by Houghton Mifflin

24. Add the following. Use a horizontal format.

$$\left(-9x^2 + 2x + 5\right) + \left(2x^2 + 4x - 9\right)$$
A) $-7x^2 + 2x - 4$
B) $-7x^2 + 6x + 4$
C) $-7x + 6x^2 - 4$
D) $-7x^2 + 6x - 4$
E) $-7x^2 + 6x - 5$

25. State whether the expression below is a monomial, a binomial, a trinomial, or none of these.

$-5a^4 - 3a$
A) Binomial
B) Trinomial
C) Monomial
D) None of these

26. Subtract the following. Use a vertical format.

$$\left(9x^2 + 10x - 2\right) - \left(4x + 12x^2 - 6\right)$$
A) $-3x^2 + 6x + 4$
B) $-3x^2 + 6x - 4$
C) $-3x + 6x^2 - 4$
D) $-3x^2 - 6x + 4$
E) $-3x^2 + 6x - 2$

27. Divide:

$$\frac{21a^2b - 3ab + 9ab^2}{3ab}$$
A) $7a - 1 + 3b$
B) $7a + 3b$
C) $7a - 1 + 3ab$
D) $7a - ab + 3b$
E) $7a - 1 + 9b$

Sample Test
Prepared by Houghton Mifflin

28. Subtract the following. Use a vertical format.

$$\left(2x^2+12x+3\right)-\left(5x^2-6x+10\right)$$

A) $-3x^2+12x-7$

B) $-3x^2+18x+7$

C) $-3x+18x^2+7$

D) $-3x^2+18x-10$

E) $-3x^2+18x-7$

29. Divide:

$$\frac{2y^2-5y-21}{y-5}$$

A) $2y+5-\dfrac{4}{y-5}$

B) $2y-5+\dfrac{4}{y-5}$

C) $2y+5+\dfrac{4}{y-5}$

D) $2y^2+5+\dfrac{4}{y-5}$

E) $2y-5-\dfrac{4}{y-5}$

30. Divide:

$$\left(2t^2-3t-14\right)\div\left(t-4\right)$$

A) $2t+5-\dfrac{6}{t-4}$

B) $2t+5+\dfrac{6}{t-4}$

C) $2t-5+\dfrac{6}{t-4}$

D) $2t^2+5+\dfrac{6}{t-4}$

E) $2t-5-\dfrac{6}{t-4}$

Sample Test
Prepared by Houghton Mifflin

31. The base of a triangle is $(2x)$ m and the height is $(4x+4)$ m.

Find the area of the triangle in terms of the variable x.

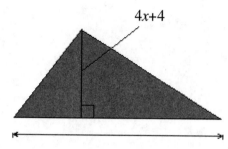

4x+4

2x

A) $4x^2 + 4x \, \text{m}^2$

B) $4x^2 + 2x \, \text{m}^2$

C) $4x^2 + 4x \, \text{m}$

D) $4x^2 + 4x \, \text{m}^2$

E) $4x^2 + 4 \, \text{m}^2$

32. Multiply:

$$-4x^3 \left(7x^2 - 5x + 1\right)$$

A) $-28x^5 - 4x^4 + 4x^3$

B) $-28x^5 + 20x^4 - 4x^3$

C) $-28x^5 + 20x^4 - 4x^3$

D) $-28x^5 + 20x^4 + 4x^3$

E) $28x^4 - 20x^5 + 4x^3$

Sample Test
Prepared by Houghton Mifflin

33. The length of a side of a square is $(4x+5)$ km.

Find the area of the square in terms of the variable x.

$4x+5$

A) $16x^2 - 40x + 25 \, \text{km}^2$
B) $16x^2 + 40x + 25 \, \text{km}^2$
C) $16x^2 + 40x + 25 \, \text{km}$
D) $16x^2 + 25 \, \text{km}^2$
E) $16x^2 + 40x - 25 \, \text{km}^2$

34. Divide:

$$\frac{5y^{11} - 2y^9 + 1}{y^4}$$

A) $5y^7 - 2y^9 + \dfrac{1}{y^4}$

B) $5y^7 - 2y^5 + y^4$

C) $5y^7 - 2y^5 + \dfrac{1}{y^4}$

D) $5y^7 - 2y^5 - \dfrac{1}{y^4}$

E) $5y^7 + 2y^5 + \dfrac{1}{y^4}$

35. Multiply:

$$\left(-3x^2 + 7x - 2\right)\left(4x - 3\right)$$

A) $-12x^3 - 37x^2 - 29x + 6$
B) $-12x^3 + 37x^2 - 29x - 6$
C) $-12x^3 + 37x^2 - 29x + 6$
D) $-12x^3 + 29x^2 - 37x + 6$
E) $-12x^3 + 37x^2 + 29x - 6$

Sample Test
Prepared by Houghton Mifflin

36. Expand:

$$(3p-7)^2$$

A) $9p^2 - 49$

B) $9p^2 + 42p + 49$

C) $9p^2 - 42p + 49$

D) $9p^2 - 42p - 49$

E) $9p^2 + 49$

37. Divide:

$$\frac{6z^2 - 15z}{-3z}$$

A) $5z - 2$

B) $z - 5$

C) $2z - 15$

D) $5 - 2z$

E) $5z - 15$

38. Multiply:

$$(2y^3 + 4y^2 + 5)(5y - 1)$$

A) $10y^4 + 18y^3 - 6y^2 + 25y - 5$

B) $10y^4 + 18y^3 - 4y^2 + 25y - 5$

C) $10y^4 + 18y^3 + 4y^2 + 25y - 5$

D) $10y^4 - 18y^3 - 4y^2 + 25y - 5$

E) $10y^4 + 18y^3 + 4y^2 - 25y - 5$

Sample Test
Prepared by Houghton Mifflin

39. The length of a rectangle is ($5x$) ft. The width is ($5x$-3) ft.

Find the area of the rectangle in terms of the variable x.

$5x$

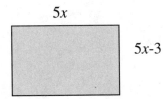

$5x$-3

A) $25x^2 + 3x$ ft^2
B) $25x^2 - 15$ ft^2
C) $25x^2 - 15x$ ft^2
D) $25x^2 - 3x$ ft^2
E) $25x^2 - 15x$ ft

40. Expand:

$$\left(2z - 2y\right)^2$$

A) $4z^2 - 4y^2$
B) $4z^2 + 8zy + 4y^2$
C) $4z^2 - 8z + 4y^2$
D) $4z^2 - 8zy + 4y^2$
E) $4z^2 + 4y^2$

Sample Test
Prepared by Houghton Mifflin

Answer Key

1. B
2. C
3. C
4. B
5. A
6. B
7. C
8. D
9. C
10. A
11. E
12. D
13. C
14. A
15. A
16. B
17. B
18. B
19. C
20. C
21. C
22. C
23. C
24. D
25. A
26. A
27. A
28. E
29. C
30. B
31. D
32. C
33. B
34. C
35. C
36. C
37. D
38. B
39. C
40. D

Sample Test
Prepared by Houghton Mifflin

Name: _____ Date: _____

1. Factor:

$$81a^2 - 72ab + 16b^2$$
A) $(4b + 9a)(4b - 9a)$

B) $(9a - 4b)^2$

C) $(9a + 4b)^2$

D) $(9ab + 4)(9ab - 4)$

E) Nonfactorable over the integers

2. Factor by grouping:

$$3c^2 - 25c - 18$$
A) $(c + 9)(3c - 2)$

B) $(c + 9)(3c + 2)$

C) $(c - 9)(3c - 2)$

D) $(c - 9)(3c + 2)$

E) Nonfactorable over the integers

3. Factor:

$$bx + 3b - 4x - 12$$
A) $(x + 3)(4 - b)$

B) $(x + 3)(b + 4)$

C) $(x + 3)(b - 4)$

D) $(x - 3)(b + 4)$

E) $(x + 4)(b - 3)$

Sample Test
Prepared by Houghton Mifflin

4. Factor:

$b^2 - 9b + 81$
A) $(b+5)(4-b)$
B) $(5b+1)(4b+1)$
C) $(b-5)(b-4)$
D) $(b+5)(b-4)$
E) Nonfactorable over the integers

5. Factor by grouping:

$10c^2 - 31c + 15$
A) $(2c+5)(5c-3)$
B) $(2c+5)(5c+3)$
C) $(2c-5)(5c-3)$
D) $(c-5)(5c+3)$
E) Nonfactorable over the integers

6. Factor:

$2bc^2 - 15bc - 27b$
A) $b(c+9)(2c-3)$
B) $b(c-9)(2c+3)$
C) $b(c-9)(2c-3)$
D) $b(c+9)(2c+3)$
E) Nonfactorable over the integers

7. The sum of the squares of two consecutive positive integers is one hundred and forty-five.

Find the two integers.
A) 12, 13
B) 6, 7
C) 10, 11
D) 8, 9
E) 9, 10

Sample Test
Prepared by Houghton Mifflin

8. Factor:

$8b^3 + 42b^2 + 27b$

A) $b(2b+9)(4b-3)$

B) $b(2b+9)(4b+3)$

C) $b(2b-9)(4b-3)$

D) $b(b-9)(4b+3)$

E) Nonfactorable over the integers

9. The height, h, in feet, that an object will attain (neglecting air resistance) in t seconds is given by $h = vt - 16t^2$, where v is the initial velocity of the object in feet per second.

A golf ball is thrown onto a cement surface and rebounds straight up. The initial velocity of the rebound is 74 ft/s.

How many seconds later will the golf ball return to the ground?

A) 8.62 s

B) 4.62 s

C) 6.62 s

D) 5.62 s

E) 3.62 s

10. Factor:

$a(9z-18)+b(9z-18)$

A) $9(z+2)(a+b)$

B) $9(z-2)(a+b)$

C) $9(z-2)(a-b)$

D) $(92-z)(a+b)$

E) Nonfactorable over the integers

Sample Test
Prepared by Houghton Mifflin

11. Solve:

$$z(z-9) = -14$$

A) 2, 7

B) 2, −7

C) −2, 7

D) −2, −7

E) No solution

12. Factor:

$$2a^2b^2 + 6ab^2 + 4b^2$$

A) $2b^2(a^2 + 3a + 2)$

B) $2b^2(a^2 + 3ab + 2b)$

C) $2b^2(a^2 + 3ab + 2)$

D) $2b^2(a^2 - 6a - 2)$

E) $2b^2(a^2 - 3a + 2)$

13. Factor:

$$4a^3b + 12a^2b^2 + 8ab^2$$

A) $4ab(a^2 + 3a + 2b)$

B) $4ab(a^2 + 3ab + 2b)$

C) $4ab(a^2 + 3ab + 2)$

D) $-4ab(a^2 - 3ab - 2b)$

E) $4ab(a + 3ab + 2b)$

Sample Test
Prepared by Houghton Mifflin

14. Factor by grouping:

$2c^2 + 7c - 15$

A) $(c+5)(2c-3)$

B) $(c+5)(2c+3)$

C) $(c-5)(2c-3)$

D) $(c+3)(2c+5)$

E) Nonfactorable over the integers

15. Factor:

$y^2(x-4)-(x-4)$

A) $y^2(x-4)-1$

B) $(y+1)^2(x-4)$

C) $(y-1)^2(x-4)$

D) $(y-1)(y+1)(x-4)$

E) Nonfactorable over the integers

16. Solve:

$x(x+2)=120$

A) 12, 10

B) 12, −10

C) −12, 10

D) −12, −10

E) No solution

17. Factor:

$5z^4 - 35z^3 + 50z^2$

A) $5z^2(z+5)(z+2)$

B) $5z(z-5)(z-2)$

C) $5z^2(z-5)(z-2)$

D) $5(z^2+5)(z^2-2)$

E) Nonfactorable over the integers

Sample Test
Prepared by Houghton Mifflin

18. Solve:

$$(z-5)(z+4)=10$$
A) 6, 5
B) −5, 6
C) −6, 5
D) −5, −6
E) No solution

19. Factor:

$$8a^3z+34za^2+21za$$
A) $za(a-7)(4a+3)$
B) $za(2a+7)(4a-3)$
C) $za(2a-7)(4a-3)$
D) $za(2a+7)(4a+3)$
E) Nonfactorable over the integers

20. Factor:

$$27a^2+6az-45a-10z$$
A) $(9a-2z)(3a-5)$
B) $(9a+3z)(2a-5)$
C) $(9a+2z)(5-3a)$
D) $(9a+2z)(3a-5)$
E) $(9a+2z)(a-5)$

Sample Test
Prepared by Houghton Mifflin

21. Factor:

$c^2 + 7c - 18$

A) $(c+9)(2-c)$

B) $(9c+1)(2c+1)$

C) $(c+9)(c+2)$

D) $(c+9)(c-2)$

E) Nonfactorable over the integers

22. Factor:

$81z^2 + 36za + 4a^2$

A) $(2a+9z)(2a-9z)$

B) $(9z-2a)^2$

C) $(9z+2a)^2$

D) $(9za+2)(9za-2)$

E) Nonfactorable over the integers

23. Factor:

$a^2 - 10a + 21$

A) $(a+7)(3-a)$

B) $(7a+1)(3a+1)$

C) $(a-7)(a-3)$

D) $(a+7)(a-3)$

E) Nonfactorable over the integers

24. The length of a rectangle is 8 in. more than twice its width. Its area is 280 in^2.

Find the length of the rectangle.

A) 27 in.

B) 28 in.

C) 29 in.

D) 784 in.

E) 280 in.

Sample Test
Prepared by Houghton Mifflin

25. Solve:

$$(2x+5)(x+1)=14$$

A) $1, -\dfrac{9}{2}$

B) $-1, -\dfrac{9}{2}$

C) $1, \dfrac{9}{2}$

D) 1, 2

E) No solution

26. Factor:

$$6c(b-4)-24x(b-4)$$

A) $6(b-4)(c+4x)$

B) $6(b-4)(4c-x)$

C) $6(b-4)(c-4x)$

D) $(b-4)(c-x)$

E) Nonfactorable over the integers

27.
The formula $S = \dfrac{n^2 + n}{2}$ gives the sum, S, of the first n natural numbers.

How many consecutive natural numbers beginning with 1 will give a sum of 10?

A) 8

B) 2

C) 6

D) 5

E) 4

Sample Test
Prepared by Houghton Mifflin

28. Factor:

$81c^2x^2 - 25$
A) $(5+9cx)(5-9cx)$
B) $(9cx-5)^2$
C) $(9cx+5)^2$
D) $(9cx+5)(9cx-5)$
E) Nonfactorable over the integers

29. The square of a positive number is six more than five times the positive number.

Find the number.
A) 11
B) 6
C) 10
D) 5
E) 15

30. Factor:

$a^2 + 85az + 36z^2$
A) $(a+2z)(4z-a)$
B) $(2a+z)(4a+z)$
C) $(a-2z)(a-4z)$
D) $(a+2z)(a-4z)$
E) Nonfactorable over the integers

31. Factor:

$-10z^3 + 150z^2 - 500z$
A) $-10z(z-10)(z-5)$
B) $-10z(z-10)(z+5)$
C) $10z(z-10)(z-5)$
D) $-10(z+10)(z-5)$
E) Nonfactorable over the integers

Sample Test
Prepared by Houghton Mifflin

32. Factor:

$$-12c^3 + 93c^2 + 135c$$

A) $-3c(c+9)(4c-5)$

B) $-3c(c+9)(4c+5)$

C) $-3c(c-9)(4c-5)$

D) $-3c(c-9)(4c+5)$

E)   Nonfactorable over the integers

33. Factor by grouping:

$$6a^2 + 29a + 28$$

A) $(2a+7)(3a-4)$

B) $(2a+7)(3a+4)$

C) $(2a-7)(3a-4)$

D) $(a-7)(3a+4)$

E)   Nonfactorable over the integers

34.

The formula $N = \dfrac{t^2 - t}{2}$ gives the number, N, of football games that must be scheduled in a league with t teams if each team is to play every other team once.

How many teams are in a league that schedules 15 games in such a way that each team plays every other team once?

A)   10

B)   4

C)   6

D)   7

E)   8

Sample Test
Prepared by Houghton Mifflin

35. Factor:

$$9 - 64x^2 y^2$$

A) $(3 + 8xy)(3 - 8xy)$

B) $(8xy - 3)^2$

C) $(8xy + 3)^2$

D) $(8xy + 3)(8xy - 3)$

E) Nonfactorable over the integers

36. The sum of two numbers is nine. The sum of the squares of the two numbers is forty-one.

Find the two numbers.
A) 4, 5
B) 6, 3
C) 8, 1
D) 2, 7
E) 5, 5

37. The distance, s, in feet, that an object falls (neglecting air resistance) in t seconds is given by $s = vt + 16t^2$, where v is the initial velocity of the object in feet per second.

An object is released from the top of a building 666 ft high. The initial velocity is 15 ft/s, and air resistance is neglected. How many seconds later will the object hit the ground?
A) 10 s
B) 4 s
C) 8 s
D) 7 s
E) 6 s

Sample Test
Prepared by Houghton Mifflin

38. Factor:

$9a^2 + 6ax - 21a - 14x$

A) $(3a - 2x)(3a - 7)$

B) $(3a + 3x)(2a - 7)$

C) $(3a + 2x)(7 - 3a)$

D) $(3a + 2x)(3a - 7)$

E) $(3a + 2x)(a - 37)$

39. Factor:

$3z^4 - 9z^3 + 6z^2$

A) $3z(z^2 - 3z + 3)$

B) $3z(3z^2 - z + 2)$

C) $3z^2(z^2 - 9z + 2)$

D) $3z^2(z^2 - 3z + 2)$

E) $3z^2(z^2 + 3z + 2)$

40. Factor:

$a(z^2 - 25) + b(z^2 - 25)$

A) $(a + b)(z - 5)^2$

B) $(a - b)(z - 5)^2$

C) $(a + b)(z + 5)^2$

D) $(a + b)(z + 5)(z - 5)$

E) Nonfactorable over the integers

Sample Test
Prepared by Houghton Mifflin

Answer Key

1. B
2. D
3. C
4. E
5. C
6. B
7. D
8. B
9. B
10. B
11. A
12. A
13. B
14. A
15. D
16. C
17. C
18. B
19. D
20. D
21. D
22. C
23. C
24. B
25. A
26. C
27. E
28. D
29. B
30. E
31. A
32. D
33. B
34. C
35. A
36. A
37. E
38. D
39. D
40. D

Sample Test
Prepared by Houghton Mifflin

Name: _____ Date: _____

1. Solve.

$$\frac{4}{7}x + 3 = 1$$

A) $-3\frac{1}{2}$

B) $-4\frac{1}{2}$

C) $-2\frac{1}{4}$

D) $-4\frac{1}{4}$

E) $-3\frac{1}{4}$

2. This year, the value of a lakefront summer cottage is $136,000. This amount is twice the value of the cottage 6 years ago. What was its value 6 years ago?
   A) $64,500
   B) $68,000
   C) $67,000
   D) $68,500
   E) $71,500

3. A sales executive earns a base monthly salary of $1000 plus a 5% commission on total sales. Find the total sales during a month in which the executive earned $32,000. Use the formula $M = S \cdot R + B$, where M is the monthly earnings, S is the total sales, R is the commission rate, and B is the base monthly salary.
   A) $2580
   B) $2530
   C) $2600
   D) $2630
   E) $2650

Sample Test
Prepared by Houghton Mifflin

4. Solve.

$$17(x-5)+2x = -8-2(x-5)$$

A) $4\dfrac{1}{4}$

B) $4\dfrac{2}{7}$

C) $5\dfrac{1}{7}$

D) $4\dfrac{1}{7}$

E) $5\dfrac{1}{4}$

5. Find the number of units made during a week when the total cost was $25,500, the cost per unit was $7, and the fixed costs were $8000. Use the formula $T = U \cdot N + F$, where T is the total cost, U is the cost per unit, N is the number of units made, and F is the fixed cost.
   A) 3125 units
   B) 2000 units
   C) 2125 units
   D) 3000 units
   E) 2500 units

6. Translate the phrase into a mathematical expression.
   The square of a number plus the product of 5 and the number
   A) $x^2 +5x^2$
   B) $(x+5)^2$
   C) $x+5x^2$
   D) $x^2 +5x$
   E) $(x+5x)^2$

7. A store manager uses a mark-up rate of 20% on all appliances. Find the cost of a blender that sells for $66.00. Round your answer to the nearest cent.
   A) $54.00
   B) $52.60
   C) $55.00
   D) $57.00
   E) $56.60

Sample Test
Prepared by Houghton Mifflin

8. Translate the phrase into a mathematical expression.
   The product of y and the sum of y and 4
   A) $y(y-4)$
   B) $y(y+4)$
   C) $\dfrac{y}{y+4}$
   D) $\dfrac{4}{4-y}$
   E) $\dfrac{y}{y-4}$

9. Sears has a pair of shoes on sale for \$64.50. This amount is \$4.75 less than the pair sells for at JC Penney's. Find the price at JC Penney's.
   A) \$69.25
   B) \$65.25
   C) \$68.75
   D) \$71.75
   E) \$76.75

10. Solve.
    $4y-13y-17=46$
    A) –9
    B) –13
    C) –7
    D) –4
    E) –2

11. Solve.
    $3x-4=9x-5$
    A) $\dfrac{1}{5}$
    B) $\dfrac{1}{7}$
    C) $\dfrac{1}{6}$
    D) 6
    E) 5

Sample Test
Prepared by Houghton Mifflin

12. Sandy's monthly salary as a sales representative was $2440. This amount included her base monthly salary of $700 plus a 3% commission on total sales. Find her total sales for the month.
    A) $51,000
    B) $58,000
    C) $55,000
    D) $62,000
    E) $65,000

13. Translate the phrase into a mathematical expression.
    9 times the difference between t and 3
    A) $9(t+3)$

    B) $9(t-3)$

    C) $t(t-3)$

    D) $\dfrac{t}{t+3}$

    E) $\dfrac{t}{t-3}$

14. Is $\dfrac{1}{3}$ a solution of $4x-1=1-7x$?
    A) Yes
    B) No
    C) Insufficient information

15. Budget Plumbing charged $360 for a water softener and installation. The charge included $280 for the water softener and $20 per hour for labor. How many hours of labor were required for the job?
    A) 5 h
    B) 3 h
    C) 4 h
    D) 6 h
    E) 7 h

Sample Test
Prepared by Houghton Mifflin

16. Translate the phrase into a mathematical expression.
    x divided by the difference between 9 and x
    A) $\dfrac{9}{9+x}$

    B) $\dfrac{x}{9+x}$

    C) $\dfrac{x}{9-x}$

    D) $x(9-x)$

    E) $9(9+x)$

17. Translate the phrase into a mathematical expression.
    The quotient of m and the difference between m and 12
    A) $12(12+m)$

    B) $\dfrac{m}{m+12}$

    C) $\dfrac{12}{12-m}$

    D) $\dfrac{12}{12+m}$

    E) $\dfrac{m}{m-12}$

18. Solve.
    $$x - \frac{11}{12} = -\frac{1}{12}$$
    A) 12

    B) $\dfrac{11}{12}$

    C) $\dfrac{13}{12}$

    D) 0

    E) $\dfrac{5}{6}$

Sample Test
Prepared by Houghton Mifflin

19. Solve.
$$\frac{4}{5}x - 1 = \frac{1}{5}x + 17$$
   A) 30
   B) 23
   C) 27
   D) 32
   E) 35

20. Solve.
$$24x + 3 = 6x + 6$$
   A) 6
   B) $\frac{1}{7}$
   C) $\frac{1}{6}$
   D) 7
   E) 8

21. The value of a sport utility vehicle this year is \$14,000, which is seven-eighths of what its value was last year. Find the value of the vehicle last year.
   A) \$19,000
   B) \$12,500
   C) \$15,500
   D) \$18,000
   E) \$16,000

22. Solve.
$$-5t - 3 = -10t - 18$$
   A) 0
   B) −10
   C) −6
   D) −3
   E) 4

Sample Test
Prepared by Houghton Mifflin

23. The price of a pair of skis at the Solitude Ski Shop is $456. This price includes the store's cost for the skis plus a mark-up at the rate of 20%. Find Solitude's cost for the skis.
    A) $370
    B) $350
    C) $380
    D) $395
    E) $405

24. Is 7 a solution of $x^2 - 10x + 4 = 4 - 3x$?
    A) Yes
    B) No
    C) Insufficient information

25. As a restaurant manager, Uechi Kim is paid a salary of $814 a week. This is $53 more per week than the salary Uechi received last year. Find the weekly salary paid to Uechi last year.
    A) $755
    B) $761
    C) $759
    D) $764
    E) $768

26. Solve.
    $5.5x - 1.5 = 26$
    A) 5
    B) 0
    C) 3
    D) 7
    E) 11

Sample Test
Prepared by Houghton Mifflin

27. Solve.

$$-5 = \frac{3}{5}t$$

A) $-8\frac{1}{3}$

B) $-7\frac{1}{3}$

C) $-7\frac{1}{6}$

D) -8

E) -9

28. Solve.

$$z + 9 = -9$$

A) 0

B) -9

C) -18

D) 9

E) 18

29. Solve.

$$1a - 6a = 8$$

A) -1

B) $-2\frac{3}{5}$

C) $-2\frac{3}{10}$

D) $-1\frac{3}{5}$

E) -3

30. Solve.

$$5m + 7m - 2 = 82$$

A) 7

B) 0

C) 6

D) 9

E) 14

Sample Test
Prepared by Houghton Mifflin

31. Find the cost per unit when the total cost was $59,000, the total number of units produced was 400, and the fixed costs were $19,000. Use the formula $T = U \cdot N + F$, where T is the total cost, U is the cost per unit, N is the number of units made, and F is the fixed cost.
    A) $130
    B) $70
    C) $85
    D) $105
    E) $100

32. McPherson Cement sells cement for $75 plus $20 for each yard of cement. How many yards of cement can be purchased for $255?
    A) 8 yd
    B) 9 yd
    C) 7 yd
    D) 11 yd
    E) 10 yd

33. Solve.
    $$x + 5(x-2) = 2(x-4) - 10$$
    A) −8
    B) −2
    C) −5
    D) 1
    E) 5

34. Solve.
    $$5 - 4(x-1) = 26(x-1)$$
    A) $1\frac{1}{3}$
    B) $1\frac{1}{6}$
    C) $2\frac{1}{6}$
    D) $1\frac{2}{7}$
    E) $2\frac{2}{7}$

Sample Test
Prepared by Houghton Mifflin

35. Translate the phrase into a mathematical expression.
11 times the total of a number and 9
A) $x(x+9)$

B) $11(x-9)$

C) $11(x+9)$

D) $\dfrac{x}{x-9}$

E) $\dfrac{x}{x+9}$

36. Tina earns a base monthly salary of $1200. Find her commission rate during a month in which the total sales were $45,800 and her earnings were $4864. Use the formula $M = S \cdot R + B$, where M is the monthly earnings, S is the total sales, R is the commission rate, and B is the base monthly salary. Round your answer to the nearest tenth of a percent.
A) 7.7%
B) 6.6%
C) 8.0%
D) 8.5%
E) 9.5%

37. Translate the phrase into a mathematical expression.
6 less than the total of 5 and a number
A) $(x-5)-6$

B) $(x+6)-5$

C) $(x-5)+6$

D) $(x-6)+5$

E) $(x+5)-6$

38. You estimate that your car can travel 395 miles on 12 gallons of gasoline. Find the miles per gallon. Round your answer to the nearest tenth of a mile per gallon.
A) 34.1 mi/gal
B) 30.7 mi/gal
C) 32.3 mi/gal
D) 33.7 mi/gal
E) 32.9 mi/gal

Sample Test
Prepared by Houghton Mifflin

39. Translate the phrase into a mathematical expression.
    4 more than three times the sum of a number and 9
    A) $9(x+3)+4$

    B) $4(x+9)+3$

    C) $4(x+3)+9$

    D) $3(x+9)+4$

    E) $9(x+4)+3$

40. Solve.
    $$3d + 2(d + 12) = -3(d - 8)$$
    A) 4
    B) −7
    C) −1
    D) 0
    E) 7

Sample Test
Prepared by Houghton Mifflin

Answer Key

1. A
2. B
3. C
4. D
5. E
6. D
7. C
8. B
9. A
10. C
11. C
12. B
13. B
14. B
15. C
16. C
17. E
18. E
19. A
20. C
21. E
22. D
23. C
24. A
25. B
26. A
27. A
28. C
29. D
30. A
31. E
32. B
33. B
34. B
35. C
36. C
37. E
38. E
39. D
40. D

Sample Test
Prepared by Houghton Mifflin

Name: _____ Date: _____

1. Simplify:

$$\sqrt{4(x+7)^2}$$

A) $2x+7$

B) $4(x+7)$

C) $2\left(\sqrt{x+7}\right)$

D) $2(x+7)$

E) $\sqrt{2}(x+7)$

2. Simplify:

$$\sqrt{27q^{21}}$$

A) $3q^{10}\sqrt{q}$

B) $3q^{10}\sqrt{3q}$

C) $3q^{9}\sqrt{3q}$

D) $3q^{100}\sqrt{q}$

E) $3q^{11}\sqrt{3q}$

3. Simplify:

$$\left(5\sqrt{x}+9\right)\left(\sqrt{x}-1\right)$$

A) $5x+4\sqrt{x}-9$

B) $5\sqrt{x}+4x-9$

C) $5x+4\sqrt{x}+9$

D) $5x-4\sqrt{x}-9$

E) $5x-4\sqrt{x}-10$

4. Simplify:

$$\left(4\sqrt{x}+11\sqrt{y}\right)\left(\sqrt{x}-\sqrt{y}\right)$$

A) $4x+7\sqrt{x}\sqrt{y}-11y$

B) $4\sqrt{x}+7xy-11\sqrt{y}$

C) $4x+7\sqrt{x}\sqrt{y}+11y$

D) $4x+7\sqrt{x}+11y$

E) $4x-7\sqrt{x}\sqrt{y}-11y$

5. Simplify:

$$\frac{\sqrt{36x^9y^8}}{\sqrt{756x}}$$

A) $\dfrac{\sqrt{21}}{21}y^4$

B) $\dfrac{\sqrt{21}}{21}x^4y$

C) $\dfrac{\sqrt{21}}{21}x^4y^4$

D) $\sqrt{21}x^4y^4$

E) $\dfrac{\sqrt{11}}{11}x^4y^4$

6. Solve and check:

$$\sqrt{y-2}-\sqrt{y-7}=1$$

A) 2

B) 11

C) 13

D) 19

E) 12

Sample Test
Prepared by Houghton Mifflin

7. Simplify:

$$\sqrt{3y}\left(\sqrt{6y}-\sqrt{y}\right)$$

A) $6y\sqrt{2}-y\sqrt{6}$

B) $3y\sqrt{2}-\sqrt{6}$

C) $3y\sqrt{2}-y\sqrt{6}$

D) $3y-y\sqrt{6}$

E) $3y\sqrt{2}-y\sqrt{3}$

8. Simplify:

$$\frac{5a^{-4}z^{-3}}{16a^{11}z^{10}}$$

A) $\dfrac{5}{16}a^{15}z^{13}$

B) $\dfrac{5}{16a^{15}z^{13}}$

C) $\dfrac{5}{16a^{13}z^{15}}$

D) $\dfrac{5}{a^{15}z^{13}}$

E) $\dfrac{5z^{13}}{16a^{15}}$

9. Simplify:

$$2x\sqrt{xy^2}-\sqrt{64x^2y^3}$$

A) $2y\sqrt{x}-8xy\sqrt{y}$

B) $2xy\sqrt{x}-8y\sqrt{y}$

C) $2xy\sqrt{x}-8xy$

D) $2xy\sqrt{x}-8xy\sqrt{y}$

E) $2xy\sqrt{y}-8xy\sqrt{x}$

Sample Test
Prepared by Houghton Mifflin

10. The measure of a big-screen television is given by the length of a diagonal across the screen. A 48-inch television has a width 38.4 in.

    Find the height of the screen to the nearest tenth of an inch.
    A) 29.7 in
    B) 28.0 in
    C) 31.8 in
    D) 29.9 in
    E) 28.8 in

11. Simplify:

    $$\sqrt{p^2 + 18p + 81}$$
    A) $p + 9$
    B) $p + 81$
    C) $\sqrt{p + 9}$
    D) $\sqrt{p} + \sqrt{9}$
    E) $p - 9$

12. Simplify:

    $$8\sqrt{19} - 2\sqrt{19} + 7\sqrt{19}$$
    A) $42\sqrt{19}$
    B) $16\sqrt{19}$
    C) $13\sqrt{19}$
    D) $6\sqrt{19}$
    E) $13\sqrt{21}$

Sample Test
Prepared by Houghton Mifflin

13. Solve and check:

$$\sqrt{8w} - 35 = 4$$

A) $\dfrac{1521}{8}$

B) $\dfrac{35}{8}$

C) $-\dfrac{1}{2}$

D) $\dfrac{1521}{64}$

E) No solution

14. A 10-foot ladder is leaning against a building.

How high on the building will the ladder reach when the bottom of the ladder is 6 ft from the building?

Round your answer to the nearest tenth.
A) 8.1 ft
B) 7.9 ft
C) 10.6 ft
D) 8.5 ft
E) 8.0 ft

15. Simplify:

$$3\sqrt{11x} + \sqrt{396x} - 12\sqrt{275x}$$

A) $-51\sqrt{11x}$

B) $-49\sqrt{11x}$

C) $49\sqrt{11x}$

D) $-51\sqrt{x}$

E) $-49\sqrt{x}$

16. Simplify:

$$\sqrt{9z^{12}y^8}$$

A) $9z^7y^4$

B) $3z^6y^4$

C) $3z^3y^4$

D) $3z^5y^4$

E) $9z^6y^4$

17. Simplify:

$$8a\sqrt{75b} - 2a\sqrt{20b} + 2a\sqrt{45b}$$

A) $2a\sqrt{5b}$

B) $24a\sqrt{3b} + 16a\sqrt{5b}$

C) $40a\sqrt{3b}$

D) $40a\sqrt{3b} + 2a\sqrt{5b}$

E) $40a\sqrt{3b} - 2a\sqrt{5b}$

18. Simplify:

$$\frac{\sqrt{2y}}{\sqrt{y}}$$

A) $\sqrt{2y}$

B) $\sqrt{y}$

C) $\sqrt{2}$

D) $\dfrac{\sqrt{2}}{y}$

E) 2

Sample Test
Prepared by Houghton Mifflin

19. Simplify:

$$12x\sqrt{3y^2} - 12y\sqrt{12x^2} - 6xy\sqrt{3}$$

A) $-18\sqrt{3xy}$

B) $-18xy^2\sqrt{3}$

C) $42xy\sqrt{3}$

D) $-18x\sqrt{3y}$

E) $-18xy\sqrt{3}$

20. Solve and check:

$$0 = 9 - \sqrt{27 + 9a}$$

A) 9

B) 8

C) No solution

D) 13

E) 6

21. Simplify:

$$12\sqrt{x} - 2\sqrt{x} + 3\sqrt{x}$$

A) $26\sqrt{x}$

B) $24\sqrt{x}$

C) $13\sqrt{x}$

D) $2\sqrt{x}$

E) $13x\sqrt{x}$

Sample Test
Prepared by Houghton Mifflin

22. Solve and check:

$$\sqrt{5b-4} = 0$$

A) $\dfrac{16}{5}$

B) $\dfrac{5}{4}$

C) $\dfrac{4}{5}$

D) $\dfrac{16}{25}$

E) No solution

23. Simplify:

$$\left(\sqrt{5}+7\right)\left(6\sqrt{5}-4\right)$$

A) $38 + 2\sqrt{5}$

B) $2 + 38\sqrt{5}$

C) $2 - 38\sqrt{5}$

D) 38

E) $38\sqrt{5}$

24. The speed of a child riding a merry-go-round at a carnival is given by the equation $v = \sqrt{12r}$, where v is the speed in feet per minute and r is the distance in feet from the center of the merry-go-round.

If the child is moving at 10 ft/s, how far is the child from the center of the merry-go-round?

Round your answer to the nearest hundredth.

A) 9.33 ft

B) 8.33 ft

C) 9.73 ft

D) 10.23 ft

E) 7.83 ft

Sample Test
Prepared by Houghton Mifflin

25. Simplify:

$$\frac{12\sqrt{3} - 6\sqrt{6}}{5\sqrt{3} + 2\sqrt{6}}$$

A) $\dfrac{84 - 54\sqrt{3}}{17}$

B) $\dfrac{84 + 54\sqrt{2}}{17}$

C) $\dfrac{84 - 54\sqrt{2}}{17}$

D) $\dfrac{84 - 54\sqrt{6}}{17}$

E) $\dfrac{84 - 54\sqrt{2}}{7}$

26. Simplify:

$$\frac{10}{\sqrt{11} - 8}$$

A) $-\dfrac{80 + 10\sqrt{11}}{53}$

B) $-\dfrac{80 + 11\sqrt{10}}{53}$

C) $-\dfrac{80 + 11\sqrt{11}}{100}$

D) $-\dfrac{80 - 10\sqrt{11}}{53}$

E) $-\dfrac{80 - 10\sqrt{11}}{53}$

27. Simplify:

$$\left(-2w^3\right)\left(w^{-5}\right)^2$$

A) $\;-\dfrac{2}{w^5}$

B) $\;2w^7$

C) $\;\dfrac{2}{w^7}$

D) $\;-\dfrac{2}{w^7}$

E) $\;-\dfrac{1}{2w^7}$

28. Solve and check:

$$\sqrt{a^2+88}=a+22$$

A) -9

B) -14

C) 1

D) -12

E) -19

29. Simplify:

$$\dfrac{\left(4r^4s^{-5}\right)^{-2}}{\left(16^{-1}r^8s^{-5}t^{-2}\right)^2}$$

A) $\;16\dfrac{s^{20}t^4}{r^{24}}$

B) $\;\dfrac{s^{20}t^4}{16r^{24}}$

C) $\;16\dfrac{s^{20}}{r^{24}t^4}$

D) $\;\dfrac{r^{24}s^{20}t^4}{16}$

E) $\;\dfrac{t^4}{16r^{24}s^{20}}$

Sample Test
Prepared by Houghton Mifflin

30. Simplify:

$$\frac{6\left(c^{-2}w^{-3}\right)^2}{19c^4w^6}$$

A) $\dfrac{6}{19}c^8w^{12}$

B) $\dfrac{6}{19c^8w^{12}}$

C) $\dfrac{6}{19c^{12}w^8}$

D) $\dfrac{6}{c^8w^{12}}$

E) $\dfrac{6w^{12}}{19c^8}$

31. Find the length of a pendulum that makes a swing in 1.8 s.

The equation for the time of one swing of a pendulum is $T = 2\pi\sqrt{\dfrac{L}{32}}$, where T is the time in seconds and L is the length in feet.

Use 3.14 for π. Round your answer to the nearest hundredth.
A) 4.63 ft
B) 2.63 ft
C) 4.93 ft
D) 4.23 ft
E) 2.53 ft

32. Simplify:

$$10\sqrt{8} - 2\sqrt{32} - 6\sqrt{50}$$

A) $-2\sqrt{2}$

B) $20\sqrt{2}$

C) $--2\sqrt{2}$

D) $42\sqrt{2}$

E) $-18\sqrt{2}$

Sample Test
Prepared by Houghton Mifflin

33. Simplify:

$$2\sqrt{432x^2} - \sqrt{48x^2}$$

A) $64\sqrt{3}x$

B) $48\sqrt{x}$

C) $20x\sqrt{3}$

D) $20\sqrt{3x}$

E) $20x$

34. Simplify:

$$\sqrt{252s^{19}b^{15}}$$

A) $6s^9b^7\sqrt{sb}$

B) $6s^9b^7\sqrt{7sb}$

C) $6s^8b^7\sqrt{7sb}$

D) $6s^9b^7\sqrt{s}$

E) $6s^{10}b^7\sqrt{7sb}$

35. Simplify:

$$\left(-7ay^2\right)\left(a^2y^{-4}\right)^2$$

A) $-\dfrac{7a^5}{y^4}$

B) $7y^6a$

C) $\dfrac{7a}{y^6}$

D) $-\dfrac{7a^5}{y^6}$

E) $-\dfrac{a^5}{7y^6}$

Sample Test
Prepared by Houghton Mifflin

36. Simplify:

$$5\sqrt{36x} - 3\sqrt{4x}$$

A) $32\sqrt{x}$

B) $12\sqrt{x}$

C) $24\sqrt{x}$

D) $6\sqrt{x}$

E) $24x$

37. Simplify:

$$\sqrt{2xy}\sqrt{8x^5 y}\sqrt{4y^2}$$

A) $8x^5 y$

B) $3x^3 y^2$

C) $8x^3 y^2$

D) $8x^5 y^2$

E) $8x^3 y$

38. Simplify:

$$\frac{\sqrt{Q} - 4}{5\sqrt{Q} + 5}$$

A) $\dfrac{Q - 5\sqrt{Q} + 4}{5Q + 5}$

B) $\dfrac{Q - 5\sqrt{Q} - 4}{5Q + 5}$

C) $\dfrac{Q - 5\sqrt{Q} + 4}{5Q - 5}$

D) $\dfrac{Q - 5\sqrt{Q} + 4}{5 - 5Q}$

E) $\dfrac{Q + 5\sqrt{Q} + 4}{5Q - 5}$

Sample Test
Prepared by Houghton Mifflin

39. How far would a submarine periscope have to be above the water to locate a ship 3 mi way?

The equation for the distance in miles that a lookout can see is $d = \sqrt{1.5h}$, where h is the height in feet above the surface of the water.

Round your answer to the nearest hundredth.
A) 6.30 ft
B) 5.20 ft
C) 6.00 ft
D) 7.00 ft
E) 6.90 ft

40. Simplify:

$$2a\sqrt{16a} + 6\sqrt{36a^3}$$

A) $26a\sqrt{a}$
B) $24\sqrt{a}$
C) $44a\sqrt{a}$
D) $18a\sqrt{a}$
E) $44a$

Sample Test
Prepared by Houghton Mifflin

Answer Key

1. D
2. B
3. A
4. A
5. C
6. B
7. E
8. B
9. D
10. E
11. A
12. C
13. A
14. E
15. A
16. B
17. D
18. C
19. E
20. E
21. C
22. C
23. B
24. B
25. C
26. A
27. D
28. A
29. A
30. B
31. B
32. E
33. C
34. B
35. D
36. C
37. C
38. C
39. C
40. C

Sample Test
Prepared by Houghton Mifflin

Sample Test
Prepared by Houghton Mifflin

Name: _____ Date: _____

1. Simplify:

$$\dfrac{\dfrac{9}{n+1}+\dfrac{1}{n}}{\dfrac{19}{n+1}+\dfrac{5}{n}}$$

A) $\dfrac{10n-1}{24n-5}$

B) $\dfrac{9n+1}{19n+5}$

C) $\dfrac{10n+1}{24n+5}$

D) $\dfrac{19n+1}{24n+5}$

E) $\dfrac{10n+9}{24n+5}$

2. On a map, two cities are $2\dfrac{5}{8}$ in. apart.

If $^3/_8$ in. on the map represents 20 mi, find the number of miles between the two cities.

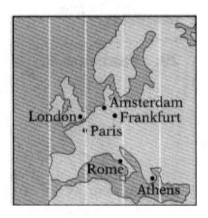

A) 136.00 mi
B) 140.00 mi
C) 156.00 mi
D) 152.00 mi
E) 138.00 mi

Sample Test
Prepared by Houghton Mifflin

3. Simplify:

$$\frac{w}{w-4}+\frac{5}{w+5}-\frac{11w-8}{w^2+w-20}$$

A) $\dfrac{21w}{w^2+w-20}$

B) $\dfrac{2w+3}{w+5}$

C) $\dfrac{w+3}{w+5}$

D) $\dfrac{w-5}{w+5}$

E) $\dfrac{w+3}{w-2}$

4. A cruise ship can sail at 27 mph in calm water. Sailing with the gulf current, the ship can sail 175 mi in the same amount of time it can sail 95 mi against the gulf current.

Find the rate of the gulf current.
A) 18 mph
B) 7 mph
C) 8 mph
D) 17 mph
E) 13 mph

5. Solve:

$$\frac{10x}{x+4}=\frac{15}{x-1}$$

A) $-\dfrac{3}{2},\dfrac{5}{2}$

B) $\dfrac{3}{2},-4$

C) $-\dfrac{3}{2},4$

D) $-\dfrac{1}{2},\dfrac{7}{2}$

E) $\dfrac{3}{2},1$

Sample Test
Prepared by Houghton Mifflin

6. Divide:

$$\frac{6-5x+x^2}{x^2-7x+10} \div \frac{x^2-9x+18}{x^2-8x+15}$$

A) $\dfrac{x+6}{x-3}$

B) $\dfrac{x-5}{x-2}$

C) $\dfrac{x+3}{x+6}$

D) $\dfrac{x-3}{x-6}$

E) $\dfrac{x-3}{x-2}$

7. An experienced painter can paint a fence twice as fast as an inexperienced painter. Working together, the painters require 4 h to paint the fence.

How long would it take the experienced painter, working alone, to paint the fence?

A) 3 h

B) 7 h

C) 8 h

D) 6 h

E) 9 h

8. Solve:

$$x + \frac{30}{x-5} = \frac{6x}{x-5}$$

A) 6

B) 5, 6

C) 30, 6

D) No solution

E) 5

Sample Test
Prepared by Houghton Mifflin

9. Simplify:

$$\frac{12t+8}{t^2+10t-12} - \frac{10t-12}{t^2+10t-12}$$

A) $\dfrac{2t}{t^2+10t-12}$

B) $\dfrac{2t+8}{t^2+10t-12}$

C) $\dfrac{2t+20}{t^2+10t-12}$

D) $\dfrac{2t-20}{t^2+10t-12}$

E) $\dfrac{-20}{t^2+10t-12}$

10. An exit poll survey showed that 5 out of every 9 voters cast a ballot in favor of an amendment to a city charter.

At this rate, how many voters voted in favor of the amendment if 9000 people voted?
A) 5200
B) 5000
C) 5900
D) 4900
E) 4300

11. Solve:

$$\frac{4x}{3} = \frac{x-14}{6}$$

A) −1
B) 7
C) 2
D) −9
E) −2

Sample Test
Prepared by Houghton Mifflin

12. Solve the formula for the given variable.

$E = IR; I$ (Physics)

A) $I = E + R$

B) $I = \dfrac{E}{R}$

C) $I = \dfrac{R}{E}$

D) $I = ER$

E) $I = E - R$

13. Simplify:

$$\dfrac{t - 5 + \dfrac{14}{t + 4}}{3t + 9 - \dfrac{6}{t + 4}}$$

A) $\dfrac{t - 1}{7}$

B) $\dfrac{t + 1}{7}$

C) $\dfrac{t - 3}{3(t + 5)}$

D) $\dfrac{(t - 1)}{3(t - 2)}$

E) $\dfrac{t - 2}{3}$

14. A plane can fly 180 mph in calm air. Flying with the wind, the plane can fly 800 mi in the same amount of time it takes to fly 640 mi against the wind.

Find the rate of the wind.

A) 23 mph

B) 24 mph

C) 20 mph

D) 21 mph

E) 27 mph

Sample Test
Prepared by Houghton Mifflin

15. A new machine can make 14,500 aluminum cans four times faster than an older machine. With both machines working, 14,500 cans be made in 20 h.

How long would it take the new machine, working alone, to make 14,500 cans?
A) 23 h
B) 25 h
C) 27 h
D) 29 h
E) 24 h

16. Find the LCM of the polynomials given below.

$3x^2 + 2x - 8$

$3x - 4$

$x + 2$
A) $(3x-4)^2(x+2)(x+3)$
B) $(x+2)(x+3)$
C) $(3x-4)(x+3)$
D) $(3x-4)(x+2)$
E) $(3x-4)(x-2)(x+3)$

17. Solve:
$$\frac{2}{x-2} = \frac{2}{2x+4}$$
A) -5
B) -1
C) -6
D) -14
E) 6

18. Two pipelines can fill a small tank in 16 min. One of the pipelines would require 48 min to fill the tank.

How long would it take the second pipeline, working alone, to fill the tank?
A) 21 min
B) 24 min
C) 29 min
D) 27 min
E) 25 min

Sample Test
Prepared by Houghton Mifflin

19. Simplify:

$$\frac{2a}{a^2-a-42}-\frac{5}{a+6}$$

A) $\dfrac{-3a}{a^2-a-42}$

B) $\dfrac{-3a+1}{a^2-a-42}$

C) $\dfrac{-3a+5}{a^2-a-42}$

D) $\dfrac{-3a-35}{a^2-a-42}$

E) $\dfrac{-3a+35}{a^2-a-42}$

20. A mechanic requires 4 h to repair a transmission, whereas an apprentice requires 12 h to make the same repairs. The mechanic worked alone for 2 h and then stopped.

How long will it take the apprentice, working alone, to complete the repairs?
A) 8 h
B) 9 h
C) 10 h
D) 6 h
E) 7 h

21. Write the fractions below in terms of the LCM of the denominators.

$$\frac{x+1}{x^2+8x-7},\ \frac{5x}{x^2-49}$$

A) $\dfrac{x^2-8x-7}{(x+7)(x-7)(x-1)},\ \dfrac{5x^2-5x}{(x+7)(x-7)(x-1)}$

B) $\dfrac{x^2-8x}{(x+7)(x-7)(x-1)},\ \dfrac{5x-5}{(x+7)(x-7)(x-1)}$

C) $\dfrac{x^2+8x+7}{(x+7)(x-7)(x-1)},\ \dfrac{5x^2-5x}{(x+7)(x-7)(x-1)}$

D) $\dfrac{x^2+8x+7}{(x+7)(x-7)(x-1)},\ \dfrac{5x^2+5x}{(x+7)(x-7)(x-1)}$

E) $\dfrac{x^2+8x+7}{(x+7)(x-7)(x+1)},\ \dfrac{5x^2-5x}{(x+7)(x-7)(x+1)}$

Sample Test
Prepared by Houghton Mifflin

22. An express train travels 406 mi in the same amount of time it takes a freight train to travel 210 mi. The rate of the express train is 28 mph faster than that of the freight train.

    Find the rate of the freight train.
    A) 30 mph
    B) 34 mph
    C) 33 mph
    D) 39 mph
    E) 37 mph

23. Triangles *ABC* and *DEF* are similar with *AB* = 7 and *DE* = 11.

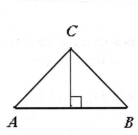 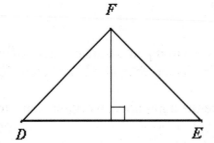

    The height of triangle *DEF* is 11. Find the area of triangle *ABC*. Round your answer to the nearest tenth.
    A) 24.5
    B) 24.9
    C) 28.3
    D) 25.6
    E) 26.8

24. Commuting from work to home, a lab technician traveled 10 mi at a constant rate through congested traffic. On reaching the expressway, the technician's speed increased by 22 mph. An additional 20 mi was traveled at the increased speed. The total time for the trip was 1 h.

    Find the rate of travel through the congested traffic.
    A) 19.4 mph
    B) 29.4 mph
    C) 22.4 mph
    D) 24.4 mph
    E) 23.4 mph

Sample Test
Prepared by Houghton Mifflin

25. Multiply:

$$\frac{2x^2 - 12x + 18}{x^2 - 7x + 12} \cdot \frac{x^2 - 7x + 12}{2x^2 - 14x + 24}$$

A) $\dfrac{x+4}{x-3}$

B) $\dfrac{x-4}{x-3}$

C) $\dfrac{x+3}{x+4}$

D) $\dfrac{x-3}{x-4}$

E) $\dfrac{x-3}{x-3}$

26. Find the LCM of the polynomials given below.

$4x^2 + 9x - 28$

$4x^2 + 5x - 21$

A) $(4x-7)^2(x+3)(x+4)$

B) $(x+3)(x+4)$

C) $(4x-7)(x+4)$

D) $(4x-7)(x+3)(x+4)$

E) $(4x-7)(x-3)(x+4)$

27. In a city of 29,000 homes, a survey was taken to determine the number with cable television. Of the 300 homes surveyed, 212 had cable television.

Estimate the number of homes in the city that have cable television.

A) 20,493

B) 20,976

C) 21,391

D) 21,398

E) 19,756

Sample Test
Prepared by Houghton Mifflin

28. The president of a company traveled 1900 mi by jet and 290 mi on a prop plane. The rate of the jet was four times the rate of the prop plane. The entire trip took a total of 5 hours.

    Find the rate of the jet plane.
    A) 612.00 mph
    B) 622.00 mph
    C) 618.00 mph
    D) 613.00 mph
    E) 619.00 mph

29. The sales tax on a car that sold for $12,000 is $840.

    At this rate, how much higher is the tax on a car that sells for $13,500?
    A) $117.00
    B) $123.00
    C) $99.00
    D) $105.00
    E) $111.00

30. Simplify:

    $$\frac{z^2 + 8z + 16}{3z^2 + 6z - 24}$$

    A) $\dfrac{z-4}{3(z+2)}$

    B) $\dfrac{z+4}{z+2}$

    C) $\dfrac{z+4}{z+2}$

    D) $\dfrac{z+4}{3(z-2)}$

    E) $\dfrac{z+4}{3(z-4)}$

Sample Test
Prepared by Houghton Mifflin

31. Triangles *ABC* and *DEF* are similar with $DE = 6$.

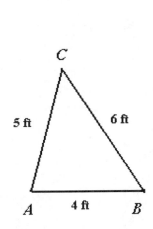
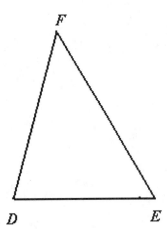

Find the perimeter of triangle *DEF*. Round your answer to the nearest hundredth.
A) 24.50 ft
B) 23.60 ft
C) 26.50 ft
D) 22.50 ft
E) 24.80 ft

32. Divide:

$$\frac{2x^2 - 14x + 24}{x^2 - 6x + 8} \div \frac{2x^2 - 18x + 36}{x^2 - 5x + 6}$$

A) $\dfrac{x+6}{x-3}$

B) $\dfrac{x-2}{x-4}$

C) $\dfrac{x+3}{x+6}$

D) $\dfrac{x-3}{x-6}$

E) $\dfrac{x-3}{x-4}$

Sample Test
Prepared by Houghton Mifflin

33. Multiply:

$$\frac{4-n^2}{n^2-6n+5} \cdot \frac{n^2+2n-35}{n^2+9n+14}$$

A) $\dfrac{7-n}{n-1}$

B) $\dfrac{2-n}{n-1}$

C) $\dfrac{2-n}{1-n}$

D) $\dfrac{7-n}{1-n}$

E) $\dfrac{1-n}{2-n}$

34. Simplify:

$$\frac{2x^2+11x+5}{2x^2+15x+25}$$

A) $\dfrac{x-1}{2(x+5)}$

B) $\dfrac{x+1}{x+5}$

C) $\dfrac{2x+1}{2x+5}$

D) $\dfrac{x+1}{2(x-5)}$

E) $\dfrac{x+1}{2(x-1)}$

Sample Test
Prepared by Houghton Mifflin

35. Write the fractions below in terms of the LCM of the denominators.

$$\frac{x-5}{x^2+9x+18}, \ \frac{x}{x^2+8x+15}$$

A) $\dfrac{x^2-25}{(x+3)(x-6)(x+5)}, \ \dfrac{x^2+6x}{(x+3)(x-6)(x+5)}$

B) $\dfrac{x^2-25}{(x+3)(x-6)(x+5)}, \ \dfrac{x^2-6x}{(x+3)(x-6)(x+5)}$

C) $\dfrac{x^2-25}{(x+3)(x+6)(x+5)}, \ \dfrac{x^2+6x}{(x+3)(x+6)(x+5)}$

D) $\dfrac{x^2+25x}{(x+3)(x+6)(x+5)}, \ \dfrac{x^2+6x}{(x+3)(x+6)(x+5)}$

E) $\dfrac{x^2-25}{(x+3)(x+6)(x+5)}, \ \dfrac{6x}{(x+3)(x+6)(x+5)}$

36. A simple syrup used in making some desserts requires 2 c of sugar for every $^2/_3$ c of boiling water.

At this rate, how many cups of sugar are required for 2 c boiling water?
A) 15
B) 10
C) 6
D) 16
E) 8

37. As part of a conservation effort for a lake, 45 fish are caught, tagged, and then released. Later 90 fish are caught. Five of the 90 fish are found to have tags.

Estimate the number of fish in the lake.
A) 812
B) 814
C) 816
D) 810
E) 828

Sample Test
Prepared by Houghton Mifflin

38. Two machines that fill cereal boxes work at the same rate. After they work for 5 h, one machine breaks down. The second machine requires 10 more hours to finish filling the boxes.

   How long would it have taken one of the machines, working alone, to fill the boxes?
   A) 22 h
   B) 21 h
   C) 24 h
   D) 23 h
   E) 20 h

39. One grocery clerk can stock a shelf in 39 min, whereas a second clerk requires 78 min to stock the same shelf.

   How long would it take to stock the shelf if the two clerks worked together?
   A) 26 min
   B) 35 min
   C) 27 min
   D) 33 min
   E) 30 min

40. Solve for x:
   $5x - y = 10$
   A) $x = 5y - 10$
   B) $x = \dfrac{y - 10}{5}$
   C) $x = \dfrac{y + 10}{5}$
   D) $x = \dfrac{1}{5}y + 10$
   E) $x = -5y - 10$

Sample Test
Prepared by Houghton Mifflin

Answer Key

1. C
2. B
3. C
4. C
5. C
6. D
7. D
8. A
9. C
10. B
11. E
12. B
13. C
14. C
15. B
16. D
17. C
18. B
19. E
20. D
21. C
22. A
23. A
24. A
25. D
26. D
27. A
28. A
29. D
30. D
31. D
32. D
33. B
34. C
35. C
36. C
37. D
38. E
39. A
40. C

Sample Test
Prepared by Houghton Mifflin

Sample Test
Prepared by Houghton Mifflin

Name: _____ Date: _____

1. Find the slope of the line containing the given points.

   $P_1(-2,0)$, $P_2(2,1)$
   A) 4
   B) $-\dfrac{1}{4}$
   C) 0
   D) 1
   E) $\dfrac{1}{4}$

2. The data in the table below show the decline in the percent of music purchased in stores in the U.S. (Source: RIAA)

   The line of best fit is $y = -3x + 55$, where x is the year (with $x = 0$ corresponding to 1997) and y is the percent of music purchased in stores in the U.S.

Year, x	1	2	3	4	5	6
Percent, y	52	51	45	42	42	37

   On a separate piece of paper graph the data and the line of best fit.

   Write a sentence that describes the meaning of the slope of the line of best fit in the context of this problem.
   A) The percent of music purchased in stores is increasing by 3% per year.
   B) The percent of music purchased in stores is decreasing by 55% per year.
   C) The percent of music purchased in stores is increasing by 55% per year.
   D) The percent of music purchased in stores is decreasing by 3% per year.
   E) The percent of music purchased in stores is changing by 3% per year.

Sample Test
Prepared by Houghton Mifflin

3. The rating (each rating point is 1,055,000 households) and share (the percentage of television sets in use tuned to a specific program) for selected television shows for a week in November 2003 are shown in the table below.

Television Show	Rating	Share
CSI	18.1	27.0
E.R.	13.6	22.0
Friends	13.4	21.0
CSI: Miami	13.2	21.0
60 Minutes	11.3	18.0

Write a relation wherein the first coordinate is the rating and the second coordinate is the share. Is the relationship a function?
   A) {(18.1, 27), (13.6, 22), (13.4, 21), (13.2, 21), (11.3, 18)};   not a function
   B) {(27, 18.1), (22, 13.6), (21, 13.4), (21, 13.2), (18, 11.3)};   a function
   C) {(27, 18.1), (22, 13.6), (21, 13.4), (21, 13.2), (18, 11.3)};   not a function
   D) {(18.1, 27), (13.6, 22), (13.4, 21), (13.2, 21), (11.3, 18)};   a function
   E) Not possible to determine using data given

4. Find the equation of the line that contains the point $(0, -1)$ and has slope -2.
   A) $y = -2x - 1$
   B) $y = -2x - 3$
   C) $y = -2x + 3$
   D) $y = 2x - 3$
   E) $y = -2x - 4$

5. Find the equation of the line that passes through the points $(2, -10)$ and $(7, -30)$.
   A) $y = 6x + 2$
   B) $y = -4x - 6$
   C) $y = 4x + 6$
   D) $y = -3x + 4$
   E) $y = -4x - 7$

Sample Test
Prepared by Houghton Mifflin

6. Graph: $y = \dfrac{3}{4}x + 2$

A)

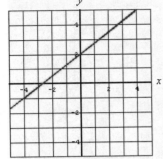

B)

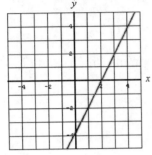

C)

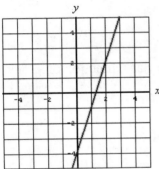

7. Determine whether the line through P_1 and P_2 is perpendicular, neither parallel nor perpendicular, or parallel to the line through Q_1 and Q_2.

$P_1(1,0)$, $P_2(3,-4)$; $Q_1(3,-6)$, $Q_2(7,-14)$

A) Perpendicular
B) Parallel
C) Neither parallel nor perpendicular

Sample Test
Prepared by Houghton Mifflin

8. Find the slope and y-intercept of the line $x + 3y = 6$.

A) $m = -\dfrac{1}{3}$, $(0, 1)$

B) $m = \dfrac{1}{3}$, $(1, 0)$

C) $m = -\dfrac{1}{3}$, $(0, -2)$

D) $m = -\dfrac{1}{3}$, $(0, 2)$

E) $m = \dfrac{1}{3}$, $(0, -2)$

9. Find the equation of the line that passes through the points $(5, 25)$ and $(7, 33)$.

A) $y = 4x - 5$

B) $y = 4x + 1$

C) $y = 4x - 1$

D) $y = 4x + 5$

E) $y = 4x + 9$

10. Does $y^4 = 2x^2 - 4$, where $x \in \{-3, -2, -1, 0\}$, define y as a function of x?

A) Yes

B) No

11. Is $(2, 6)$ a solution of $y = 5x - 5$?

A) No

B) Yes

12. Find the equation of the line that passes through the points $(0, 3)$ and $(-5, 6)$.

A) $y = -\dfrac{3}{5}x + 3$

B) $y = -\dfrac{5}{3}x - 3$

C) $y = 3x + 3$

D) $y = -\dfrac{3}{5}x - 3$

E) $y = \dfrac{5}{3}x + 3$

Sample Test
Prepared by Houghton Mifflin

13. Graph by using the slope and y-intercept: $x + y = 2$

A)

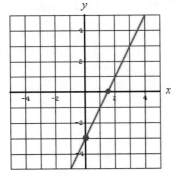

B)

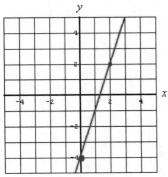

C)

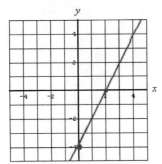

Sample Test
Prepared by Houghton Mifflin

14. Find the *x*- and *y*-intercepts and then graph: $x + y = 2$

   A) *x*-intercept: (2, 0), *y*-intercept: (0, 2)

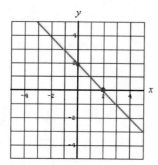

   B) *x*-intercept: (0, 0), *y*-intercept: (0, 0)

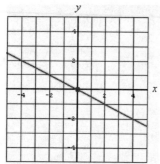

   C) *x*-intercept: (0, 0), *y*-intercept: (0, 0)

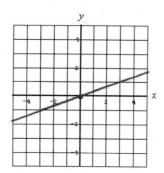

Sample Test
Prepared by Houghton Mifflin

15. Find the *x*- and *y*-intercept and then graph: $y = \dfrac{3}{4}x + 2$

A) *x*-intercept: (2, 0), *y*-intercept: (0, 2)

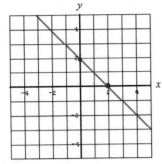

B) *x*-intercept: (3/2, 0), *y*-intercept: (0, –3)

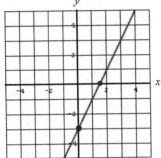

C) *x*-intercept: (-8/3, 0), *y*-intercept: (0, 2)

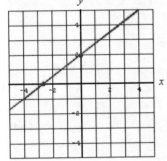

16. A custom-illustrated sign or banner can be commissioned for a cost of $23.00 for the material and $11.80 per square foot for artwork. The equation that represents this cost is given by $y = 11.80x + 23.00$, where *y* is the cost and *x* is the number of square feet in the sign. Graph this equation for $0 \le x \le 20$.

Write a sentence that describes the meaning of the ordered pair (20, 259.00), which is on the graph.
A) It costs $20 for a custom sign 259.00 ft^2 in area.
B) It costs $259.00 for a custom sign 20 ft^2 in area.

Sample Test
Prepared by Houghton Mifflin

17.
Given the function $s(t) = \dfrac{3}{4t-2}$, find $s(-3)$.

A) $-\dfrac{3}{14}$

B) 3

C) $\dfrac{3}{14}$

D) $-\dfrac{1}{5}$

E) 0

Sample Test
Prepared by Houghton Mifflin

18. Graph: (3, 3)

A)

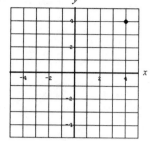

B)

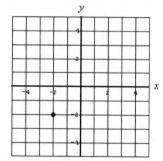

C)

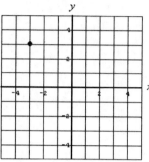

D)

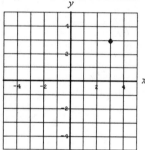

E)

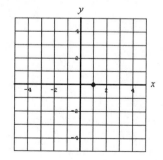

Sample Test
Prepared by Houghton Mifflin

19. Graph: $-a\,x - y = 2$

A)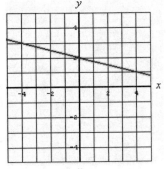

B)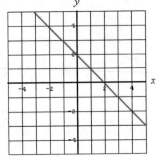

C)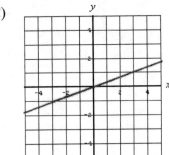

20. Given the function $f(x) = 3x\ -5x - 5$, find $f(-5)$.

   A) 10
   B) 2
   C) 5
   D) 8
   E) 1

21. Name the ordinate of the point shown below.

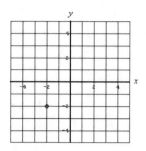

A) 1
B) −1
C) −4
D) −3
E) −2

22. Graph: $x = 1$

A)

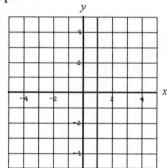

B)

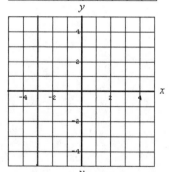

C)

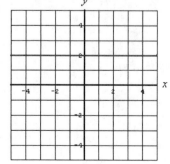

Sample Test
Prepared by Houghton Mifflin

23. Find the coordinates of the point shown below.

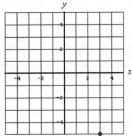

   A) $(3, 5)$
   B) $(4, 5)$
   C) $(3, 4)$
   D) $(2, 5)$
   E) $(3, 6)$

24. Find the x- and y-intercepts of the line $y = -3x - 3$.
   A) $(-3, 0)$, $(0, -2)$
   B) $(0, -3)$, $(-2, 0)$
   C) $(-1, 0)$, $(0, -3)$
   D) $(-3, 0)$, $(0, 2)$
   E) $(-1, 0)$, $(0, 3)$

Sample Test
Prepared by Houghton Mifflin

25. Graph: $y = x$

A)

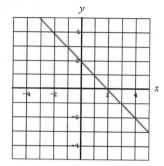

B)

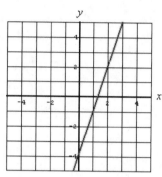

C)

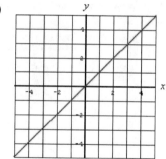

26. A rescue helicopter is rushing at a constant speed of 150 mph to reach several people stranded in the ocean 11 mi away after their boat sank. The rescuers can determine how far they are from their victims using the equation $D = 12 - 2.4t$, where D is the distance in miles and t is the time elapsed in minutes. Graph this equation for $0 \leq t \leq 4$. The point $(2, 7.2)$ is on the graph.

Write a sentence that describes the meaning of this ordered pair.
A) After flying for 2 min, the helicopter is 7.2 mi away from the victims.
B) After flying for 7.2 min, the helicopter is 2 mi away from the victims.
C) The helicopter is 2 mi away from the victims after flying 7.2 mi.
D) After flying for 2 mi, the helicopter is 7.2 minutes away from the victims.

27. Name the abscissa of the point shown below.

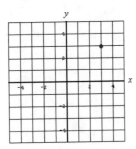

A) 3
B) 4
C) 1
D) 2
E) 6

28. Graph: $x + 4y = 8$

A)

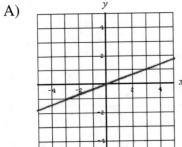

B)

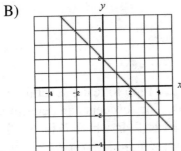

C)

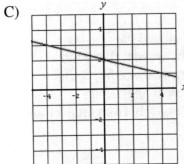

Sample Test
Prepared by Houghton Mifflin

29. Find the ordered-pair solution of $-2x + 3y = 6$, $x = -3$.
    A) $(-3, 0)$
    B) $(-3, 2)$
    C) $(-3, -3)$
    D) $(0, -3)$
    E) $(-3, 0)$

30. Find the equation of the line that passes through the points $(0, 0)$ and $(-5, -3)$.
    A) $y = \dfrac{3}{5}x$
    B) $y = \dfrac{5}{3}x$
    C) $y = 3x$
    D) $y = -\dfrac{3}{5}x$
    E) $y = -\dfrac{5}{3}x$

Sample Test
Prepared by Houghton Mifflin

31.

Graph by using the slope and y-intercept: $y = \dfrac{1}{3}x$

A)

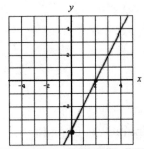

B)

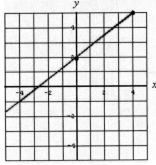

C)

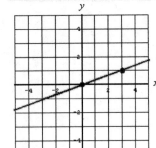

32.

Find the equation of the line that contains the point $(-7, 3)$ and has slope $\dfrac{2}{7}$.

A) $y = \dfrac{2}{7}x + 5$

B) $y = -\dfrac{2}{7}x + 5$

C) $y = -\dfrac{2}{7}x - 10$

D) $y = \dfrac{2}{7}x - 10$

E) $y = -\dfrac{2}{7}x - 7$

Sample Test
Prepared by Houghton Mifflin

33. Find the slope and y-intercept of the line $-x + -2y = -6$.

A) $m = -\dfrac{1}{2}$, $(0, 5)$

B) $m = \dfrac{1}{2}$, $(5, 0)$

C) $m = -\dfrac{1}{2}$, $(0, 3)$

D) $m = -\dfrac{1}{2}$, $(0, -5)$

E) $m = \dfrac{1}{2}$, $(0, -3)$

34. Graph: $y = 2$

A)

B)

C)

Sample Test
Prepared by Houghton Mifflin

35. Graph: $y = 2x - 4$

A)

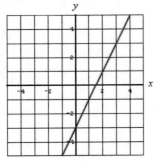

B)

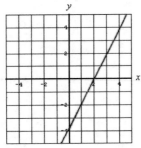

C)

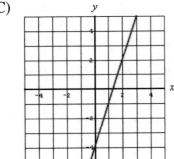

36. The data in the table below show the number of carbohydrates used for various amounts of time during a strenuous tennis workout. The line of best fit is $y = 1.51x + 3.44$, where x is the time in minutes and y is the number of carbohydrates used in grams.

Time of workout, x (in minutes)	5	10	20	30	60
Carbohydrates used, y (in grams)	10	20	33	49	94

On a separate piece of paper graph the data and the line of best fit.

Write a sentence that describes the meaning of the slope of the line of best fit in the context of this problem.
A) The tennis player is using 1.51 g of carbohydrates per hour.
B) The tennis player is using 3.44 g of carbohydrates per minute.
C) The tennis player is using 1.51 g of carbohydrates per game.
D) The tennis player is using 1.51 g of carbohydrates per minute.
E) The tennis player is using 3.44 g of carbohydrates for every 5 minutes of play.

Sample Test
Prepared by Houghton Mifflin

37.
Find the equation of the line that contains the point $(0, -4)$ and has slope $-\dfrac{5}{16}$.

A) $\quad y = \dfrac{5}{16}x - 4$

B) $\quad y = -\dfrac{5}{16}x - 4$

C) $\quad y = -\dfrac{5}{16}x + 3$

D) $\quad y = \dfrac{5}{16}x + 3$

E) $\quad y = -\dfrac{5}{16}x + 2$

38.
Graph: $y = -\dfrac{1}{2}x$

A)

B)

C)

Sample Test
Prepared by Houghton Mifflin

39. Find the equation of the line that contains the point (4, –23) and has slope –5.
    A) $y = 5x - 8$
    B) $y = -5x - 8$
    C) $y = -5x - 3$
    D) $y = 5x - 8$
    E) $y = -5x - 9$

40. The pressure, in pounds per square inch, on a diver is shown in the graph to the right.

    Find the slope, m, of the line.

    Write a sentence that explains the meaning of the slope.

    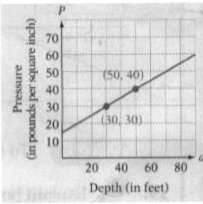

    A) $m = 2$. For each additional foot a diver descends below the surface of the water, the pressure on the diver increases by 2 pounds per square inch.
    B) $m = 0.5$. For each additional foot a diver descends below the surface of the water, the pressure on the diver increases by 0.5 pound.
    C) $m = 0.5$. For each additional foot a diver descends below the surface of the water, the pressure on the diver decreases by 0.5 pound per square inch.
    D) $m = 0.5$. For each additional foot a diver descends below the surface of the water, the pressure on the diver increases by 0.5 pound per square inch.
    E) $m = 0.5$. For each additional foot a diver descends below the surface of the water, the pressure on the diver increases by 0.5 pound per square foot.

Answer Key

1. E
2. D
3. D
4. A
5. D
6. A
7. B
8. D
9. D
10. B
11. A
12. A
13. C
14. A
15. C
16. B
17. A
18. C
19. B
20. C
21. E
22. A
23. A
24. C
25. C
26. A
27. A
28. C
29. A
30. A
31. C
32. A
33. C
34. B
35. B
36. D
37. B
38. A
39. C
40. D

Sample Test
Prepared by Houghton Mifflin